ALBRECHT DVRER
Master Printmaker

Department of Prints & Drawings

Museum of Fine Arts

Boston, Massachusetts

Copyright © 1971 by the Museum of Fine Arts, Boston, Massachusetts

All rights reserved

Library of Congress Catalogue No. 77-183708

Typeset in Linofilm Palatino by Wrightson Typographers, Boston

Printed by The Meriden Gravure Co., Meriden, Connecticut

Designed by Barbara Hawley and Carl Zahn

Dates of the exhibition:

November 17, 1971 through January 16, 1972

NE
654
D9
B63

ACKNOWLEDGMENTS

This catalogue was produced by the collaborative effort of the staff and volunteers of the Department of Prints and Drawings. Each contributor has helped the others with information, friendly criticism, and some rewriting and has, in turn, been edited by them. It is possible, therefore, to designate only in a general way areas of primary responsibility. Eleanor A. Sayre wrote the Introduction and, with the assistance of Clifford S. Ackley and Sue W. Reed, served as departmental editor for the catalogue. The supplementary list of the entire collection of Dürer's prints was made by Stephanie E. Loeb. She also wrote the entries on the woodcuts, with the exception of catalogue numbers 63–82 and 159–165, which were prepared by Barbara S. Shapiro. The entries on Dürer's books were written by Wendy T. Topkins. The entries on the engravings were written by Mrs. Reed, except for number 62, by David H. Solkin, and numbers 86–89, 109, 183, and 185, by Mr. Ackley. He was also responsible for the entries on the etchings and drypoints. Huston Paschal helped with various problems of research. For months Karin A. Peltz undertook manifold duties which kept the Print Room functioning; she was assisted by Jean Cadogan. At a critical point in the catalogue's writing when the curator was confined to a hospital, Rachel Wheeler gave advice and served as amanuensis. We are indebted to former members of the department for much preliminary research, to Henry P. Rossiter and Anna H. Mavor, and most recently to Carlene H. Soller. The conservators, Francis W. Dolloff and Roy L. Perkinson, made major contributions by their careful examination of the prints for condition and by answering questions on technique. Mr. Perkinson contributed information on the manufacture and care of paper. We also consulted Cyril S. Smith, professor of metallurgy at the Massachusetts Institute of Technology.

The following colleagues at other institutions have also helped us: Karel Boon, Rijksmuseum, Amsterdam; Ruth S. Magurn, Fogg Art Museum, Harvard University, and Philip Hofer, Peter A. Wick, and Eleanor Garvey, Houghton Library, Cambridge, Mass.; John Rowlands, British Museum, and Arthur Driver, P. & D. Colnaghi, Ltd., London; Richard S. Field, Philadelphia Museum of Art. We are especially grateful to Charles W. Talbot, Gaillard F. Ravenel, and Jay A. Levenson, the organizers of the exhibition *Dürer in America*, which was held at the National Gallery of Art, Washington, D.C., in the spring of 1971. They were most generous with their information and lent their catalogue to us while it was still in manuscript form.

Many members of the Museum staff assisted in the preparation of the catalogue: Carl Zahn, Ellen Farrow as editor and Barbara Hawley as designer.

We are indebted to the Meriden Gravure Company, as we have been in the past, for the extra pains they have taken with reproductions.

The installation of the exhibition was designed by Tom Wong.

Diggory Venn helped the project in many ways, particularly in securing a grant from the National Endowment for the Arts, Washington, D.C., a federal agency. They supported in part both the catalogue and the exhibition.

CHRONOLOGY

<table>
<tr><td>1471–1485</td><td>Born in Nuremberg; baptized, with the publisher Anton Koberger as godfather; trains as a goldsmith with his father</td></tr>
<tr><td>1486–1489</td><td>Apprenticeship to the painter Michael Wolgemut, who was also involved in publishing illustrated books</td></tr>
<tr><td>1490–1494</td><td>Travels: may have visited Housebook Master; goes to Colmar in 1492 hoping to see Schongauer, who had died; stays in two book publishing centers, Basel and Strassburg</td></tr>
<tr><td>1494</td><td>Returns to Nuremberg; marries Agnes Frey; sets out for Venice</td></tr>
<tr><td>1495–1500</td><td>Returns to Nuremberg; intense activity in engravings and woodcuts</td></tr>
<tr><td>1498</td><td>Publishes the Apocalypse</td></tr>
<tr><td>1505–1507</td><td>Second trip to Venice; travels at least as far as Bologna</td></tr>
<tr><td>1509–1511</td><td>Great productivity in woodcuts; 1511 publishes the Small Passion, Large Passion, and Life of the Virgin, and reprints the Apocalypse</td></tr>
<tr><td>1512</td><td>Experiments with drypoint</td></tr>
<tr><td>1512–1522</td><td>Works on commissions for the Emperor Maximilian</td></tr>
<tr><td>1513–1514</td><td>Intense activity in engraving, including Knight, Death, and the Devil; Saint Jerome in His Study; and Melencolia I</td></tr>
<tr><td>about
1514–1518</td><td>Experiments with etching</td></tr>
<tr><td>1520–1521</td><td>Journeys to the Netherlands; keeps a journal that contains much information concerning his prints</td></tr>
<tr><td>1525 & 1527</td><td>Publishes two treatises he has written: on the art of measurement (Underweysung der Messung) and on fortification (Befestigung)</td></tr>
<tr><td>1528</td><td>Dies at Nuremberg; posthumous publication of his treatise on human proportion (Vier Bücher von Menschlicher Proportion)</td></tr>
</table>

INTRODUCTION

The Dürer Collection

To celebrate the five hundredth anniversary of Albrecht Dürer's birth at Nuremberg in 1471, the Department of Prints and Drawings decided some time ago to arrange an exhibition of his prints, drawing exclusively upon the fine collection of his work in the Museum of Fine Arts, Boston. This exhibition, *Albrecht Dürer: Master Printmaker,* follows the point of view of the 1969 exhibition, *Rembrandt: Experimental Etcher,* in which multiple impressions and comparisons between prints of fine and lesser quality were shown.

The Print Room has adhered to the sound principle laid down in the nineteenth century by its first curator, Sylvester Rosa Koehler: a well-stocked print room should contain not only the finest examples of prints by great and minor masters but should have, as often as possible, contrasting examples of the same print. For this reason the Print Room has rarely sold its duplicates but has retained them for the education of scholar, connoisseur, and novice alike. An exhibition of this nature is possible only with such resources to draw from.

The two hundred and twenty-one objects selected for this exhibition were acquired from 1892, when the Museum was given a set of the engraved *Passion,* to 1971, when several notable purchases were made. In 1897 the Museum was able, through the bequest of Harvey D. Parker, to purchase the entire Henry F. Sewall collection of prints. Among them were the one hundred and seventy Dürers included in the complete list of the Museum's collection at the end of this catalogue. A number of very beautiful impressions have been given or bequeathed to the Department at various times by donors — singly, such as the brilliant one given by Mrs. W. Scott Fitz, or as groups, given by members of the Bullard family and by W. G. Russell Allen and his niece Lydia Evans Tunnard. Throughout this period the Museum has steadfastly sought to improve the quality of the collection through purchase. In 1930, a pair of drypoints, as fine as they are rare, were acquired from Richard Zinser.

In 1968, an important part of the fine Tomás Harris collection was acquired by purchase and through the generosity of a Trustee, Landon T. Clay. It was arranged that the rest of the collection be purchased by the Sterling and Francine Clark Institute, Williamstown, Mass.

Because so much of the information in the catalogue depends on a clear understanding of technical terms and the processes of printmaking, those matters as they pertain to Dürer's woodcuts and intaglio prints are discussed first.

Print Processes and Impressions

Intaglio: Engraving, Etching, and Drypoint

Metal plates in which the lines are not flush with the surface but below it are called *intaglio* plates. Lines can be incised (*engraving*), bitten with acid (*etching*), or scratched with a sharp, pointed tool (*drypoint*) into the plate.

In an *engraving,* the artist uses the sharp, lozenge-shaped tip of the graver, or burin, to cut V-shaped troughs into a plate, usually of copper. For very fine lines, he makes a shallow incision; for heavier lines, he makes a wider, deeper cut into the metal. When these lines are printed, they have an inherent, firm clarity. By varying the force and depth of cutting, any single line can be made to swell or diminish and be used to suggest the shadowed edge of an object, a potential of the medium which Dürer's great German predecessor, Martin Schongauer, was the first to exploit (figs. 1 and 8).

In an *etching,* the plate is covered with a waxy compound through which one can draw very easily, exposing the metal where there is to be a line. The plate is then bathed with acid, which eats into the exposed metal. The relative strength of the lines will depend primarily on whether the biting is brief, which produces a narrow, shallow trough barely etched into the surface, or prolonged, which produces a deeper, wider trough. Since acid cannot bite as neatly as a graver can cut, the edges of an etched line when printed will be slightly rougher than an engraved line (fig. 2).

The great pressure used in printing intaglio plates causes the metal to be compressed microscopically each time an impression is taken. With repeated printings, the very fine, shallow lines are the first to disappear and after them, intermediate ones. Eventually only the broad, deep lines remain, leaving merely the bare bones of what was originally engraved or etched into the plate (cat. nos. 86–88).

Drypoint lines are not cut deeply into the plate but are lightly scratched on its surface with a needle-sharp tool, allowing an artist to draw with a freedom approaching that of the etcher. For this reason, the drypoints printed by the Northern fifteenth-century printmaker, the Housebook Master, are quite comparable in style of execution to his drawings (fig. 6). Because drypoint lines lie so close to the surface of the plate, their printing life is brief. This is probably the reason why, despite the obvious fascination his prints held for his contemporaries, including the young Dürer, no more than five impressions of any of the Housebook Master's subjects have been preserved. The drypoint medium has a potential that Dürer was the first to exploit

Fig. 1

Fig. 3

Fig. 2

Fig. 1. Engraved lines (detail of *The Combat of Hercules,* cat. no. 15)

Fig. 2. Etched lines (detail of the *Agony in the Garden,* cat. no. 191)

Fig. 3. Drypoint lines (detail of *Saint Jerome by the Pollard Willow,* cat. no. 175)

Fig. 4. Woodcut lines (detail of *Hercules,* cat. no. 17)

Fig. 4

fully. The needle can be held at such an angle that burr, or curled edges of cut metal, will be raised up on the surface of the plate. They hold the ink and print as rich, velvety lines capable of great modulation and a wide variety of effects (fig. 3). Unfortunately, the burr wears away, leaving only a faint, delicate, unadorned line.

Metal plates have frailties that time and use affect. Light scratches, which may be caused either by the initial polishing or by the subsequent inking and wiping of a plate, appear and disappear throughout its printing history (cat. nos. 3–5 and 179–181, respectively). Deep accidental scratches also occur which persist (cat. no. 2). Sometimes, when such a scratch is particularly disturbing, an attempt is made to remove it, though traces of it usually remain (cat. nos. 177–178). When metal plates are not properly cared for, they may also corrode (cat. nos. 180–181 and 191–192). When the image had become significantly weaker as a result of years of continued printing, worn copper plates were often reworked by a craftsman. Usually he attempted merely to deepen the outlines and most important parts of the shading, but he was not always able to follow the lines precisely (cat. nos. 177–178).

Relief: Woodcut

When a woodblock is cut, the areas that are intended to print stand out in relief, while the surrounding areas are cut away. Lines that print are wedge-shaped ridges whose narrow, flat tops receive the printing ink. When freshly cut, the tops of these ridges have sharp outer edges, so that lines printed from a new woodblock often make slight indentations in the paper and have clear, crisp contours (fig. 4). As impressions are pulled, the repeated pressure exerted on the block causes the ridges to gradually broaden and lose their initial sharpness. Consequently, in these later impressions, the forcefulness of the printed lines begins to disappear, contours of objects lose precision, and details seen in shadow become increasingly illegible.

With the passage of time, various accidents occur that also detract from the quality of the impressions. As the woodblock ages and dries, a join may begin to open or a crack to form, leaving a fine white line cutting across part of the design. Aggravated by continual variations in humidity, such a crack will widen and lengthen, slowly pushing its way from one edge of the block to the other (cat. nos. 19–21). The block itself may warp, so that it cannot print evenly in a press. Scratches and dents on the surface of the block produce tiny spots of white in the black lines of the print (cat. no. 70). The most fragile or isolated of the ridges on the woodblock are likely to break off segment by segment. Woodworms, too, may attack the block, causing roundish spots of white to appear in the print (cat. no. 21).

When the block has become such a ruin that few care any longer to buy the crude image it can produce, the owner may choose to destroy it. But if the artist's name alone can still sell prints, a publisher may have the block repaired and perhaps commission a craftsman to recut and clarify important lines that have thickened.

Paper

For qualities of beauty, permanence, and durability, the printing papers available to Dürer have never been surpassed, even though knowledge of the art of papermaking had come to Germany less than a century before Dürer began his apprenticeship. A papermill established in Nuremberg in 1390 may have been the first in that part of Europe, although papermaking was practiced in Italy in the twelfth century. Fifteenth- and sixteenth-century paper was made by hand from linen rags, without the use of modern chemical bleaching agents. It was strong and durable; had a pleasing, warm, ivory or cream white color; and possessed a lively resilience and rich surface texture quite unlike any of today's machine-made papers.

Paper is, however, a vulnerable material, and there are many factors, both natural and man-made, that can adversely affect its condition and appearance. Either before or during printing, creases can occur which may produce irregularities or abrupt discontinuities in the image (cat. no. 52). The growth of mold causes rust-colored spots called "foxing" (cat. no. 2). Traces of old glue may show as brown stains (cat. nos. 93–108). The original color of the paper may be reduced to an unnatural whiteness by injudicious cleaning (see the introduction to cat. nos. 63–82 in reference to the Evans set). The embossed quality of woodcuts may virtually disappear if they are subjected to great pressure during restoration. Holes and tears may detract from the appearance of a print, although in some cases skillful repair may render them almost unnoticeable (cat. no. 217). Years of careless handling often result in abrasions of the surface that may severely diminish the clarity of the printed image. Even what was once a fine early impression, when badly abused and generally soiled, may appear to be a much later one (cat. no. 51).

Impressions

The basic elements of a print are the white of the paper and the black of printed lines. As the block or plate wears, the original relationship of these elements inevitably shifts as the fine lines of a copper plate weaken and disappear or the lines of a woodblock coarsen. A print executed by an artist of little or no ability can tolerate a certain amount of such deterioration. In a print by a competent artist who has conceived the whole pattern of relationships with care, this distortion is soon apparent; thus his true capability can be judged only in reasonably early impressions. In prints executed by a great printmaker, such as Dürer, who has learned his art well, the earliness of the impression is even more important. He will have used both intuition and extraordinary intelligence to predetermine the ideal balance of elements for each of his prints. It is the very acuteness of that balance which causes even a slight shift in the condition of the printing surface to be damaging to the visual effect.

It is obvious, then, to any connoisseur, that Dürer's prints cannot be comprehended fully without intimate knowledge of a number of early, brilliant impressions. And here we are presented with a difficulty, for it must be admitted that despite his strong bent toward perfectionism, in practice, Dürer showed no signs at all of conforming to this modern point of view. In 1523, for example, he sent to Cardinal Albrecht of Brandenburg the lightly engraved copper plate of his portrait (cat. no. 215), together with five hundred prints taken from it—far too many for the plate to have produced without serious losses (Conway, p. 128). It might be pointed out that these were probably intended as book plates. However, during the Netherlands journey of 1520–21, Dürer was received with great honor by patron and artist alike and plainly wanting to reciprocate, would often give an impression of the 1514 *Saint Jerome in his Study*. It is even more surprising to read of his presenting the Factor of Portugal with impressions of prints he had executed at the turn of the century, the *Saint Eustace* of about 1501 (cat. no. 59) and *The Nativity* of 1504 (cat. no. 86) (Conway, p. 100).

In the twentieth century, there is no way to determine how much the impoverishment of the image mattered to Dürer. Possibly, like any thrifty German citizen, he was reluctant to forego any chance of profit; perhaps he believed that his own great skill of hand and his knowledge of art would far surpass the work of his contemporaries however worn the given impression.

Dürer's Education as a Printmaker

It was Dürer's intent to publish a monumental work on the theory and practice of art, not in Latin but in the German vernacular. Parts of this project were published during his lifetime: in 1525, the *Underweysung der Messung* (Teaching of Measurement) cat. nos. 218–219, written with a greater clarity and vividness of terminology than that of professional geometricians of the time; in 1527, the *Etliche underricht, zu befestigung* (on fortification) cat. no. 220; and four sections dealing with the proportions of human beings, (*Vier Bücher von Menschlicher Proportion*) cat. no. 221, were published posthumously. But much of what Dürer intended to say remained in manuscript: written, crossed out, rewritten and corrected, or left in outline form. From one of his outlines we learn that he planned to discuss the temperament and the best education for the ideal painter. "Note should be taken," he wrote, "of the birth of the child, in what sign it occurreth . . . Pray God for a lucky hour" (Conway, p. 171).

His own birth was recorded by his father: "*Item,* in the year 1471 after the birth of Christ, in the sixth hour of the day, on Saint Prudentia's day, a Tuesday in Passion Week, my wife bare me my second son. His godfather was Anton Koburger [sic], and he named him Albrecht after me" (Conway, p. 34).

However the relevant astrological signs may have been interpreted in his day, it is clear that the younger Albrecht was indeed fortunate at birth. He was endowed with a precocious artistic ability to which his haunting self-portrait, drawn at the age of thirteen, testifies. In addition, he was by temperament diligent, curious, and intellectual; and he was to grow up and practice his profession in Nuremberg at a time when the intellectual and artistic life of the city was vigorous.

He was the third child of a goldsmith, a man who, Dürer tells us, had trained in the Netherlands with the "great masters." Dürer's father expected his son to enter his own shop, and taught him at an early age to handle a goldsmith's tools with precision. It is essential to understand the importance of this skill acquired in childhood, for it was in the workshops of craftsmen who incised decorations on objects of precious metal that some of the most interesting early engravings were produced. Dürer was to become one of the small number of great, innovative engravers, but the foundation for his achievements must certainly be credited to his father.

By the time Dürer was fifteen, he had persuaded his father to allow him to be a painter; on November 30, 1486, he was apprenticed to Michael Wolgemut. Set against the accomplishments of his fellow citizens, in the exhibition held in 1971 in Nuremberg, Wolgemut does not seem to have been a painter or draughtsman of very marked ability, although his workshop was widely known. However, his interests were broader than painting, and he was involved in publishing books illustrated with woodcuts designed by professional painters not, as was the common practice, by craftsmen. These books were printed for him by Dürer's godfather, Anton Koberger. In these two shops there was an opportunity for Dürer to learn from beginning to end the arts of designing, cutting, and printing woodblocks.

Dürer ended his apprenticeship to Wolgemut late in 1489, and in April 1490, he left Nuremberg, remaining away for four years. It is possible that he visited an artist whose name has not survived and who is known to us as the Housebook Master. It is plain that the drypoints of this gifted, inventive artist influenced Dürer stylistically as a young man, and technically later on. Early in 1492, he went to Colmar to learn what he could from another great printmaker, Martin Schongauer, whose engravings had a marked influence on him. But when he arrived, Schongauer had died, and Dürer saw only his three less talented brothers.

Later that year, Dürer was in Basel, a book publishing center. There he designed the one woodcut in this period of his life which can be attributed to him with absolute certainty, since his signature is still preserved on the back of the block. The vigorous but simple design was published in 1492 as a frontispiece to Saint Jerome's *Epistolare* (fig. 5). Dürer is thought to have stayed also in Strassburg, another publishing center. In May 1494, he returned to Nuremberg, just before his twenty-third birthday.

Other books published in these two cities, as well as in Nuremberg, are believed to contain woodcut illustrations designed by Dürer. Some of these woodcuts have been ascribed to him on credible stylistic grounds. An equally sound basis for believing him to have engaged in such activity is the striking development visible between the *Saint Jerome* of 1492 and the unsigned but universally accepted *Hercules* of about 1496 (cat. no. 17). Although the museum owns some of the books in question, they have not been included because the exhibition is more concerned with Dürer as an independent, inventive printmaker.

Fig. 5. Frontispiece to Saint Jerome's *Epistolare* (Basel, 1492) woodcut. Anonymous collection.

Stylistic Development in Dürer's Intaglio Prints

In 1494 Dürer, in the spring, had completed his traditional bachelor's journey; in the summer, had taken a wife; and, in the autumn, had gone, by himself, to spend the winter in Italy (a very uncommon journey for a fifteenth-century Northern painter). He returned to Nuremberg in 1495, and it is at this juncture in his life that the exhibition begins.

What is believed to be the earliest print in the exhibition is an engraving of about 1495, *Young Woman Attacked by Death* (cat. no. 1). It is surprising to find in this work no reflection of the Italian Renaissance compositions Dürer had just seen, admired, and on occasion, copied. The energy, the contrast of pungent black lines and white paper, and the lively complexity of form in this small print spring directly from Northern tradition, specifically the drypoints of the Housebook Master (fig. 6). In style, however, it is most closely related to Dürer's own early drawings.

Dürer's early engravings owe much to Schongauer. The latter's breadth of subject matter, the originality of his designs, and his ordered, lucid draughtsmanship were so impressive that his prints were widely imitated and copied. Schongauer's engraved line was equally inventive, as can be seen in *Two Turks* (fig. 7). Instead of using his burin to engrave lines of even width in the copper (like the lower borderline), he had learned to make them taper and swell, thus forcing them to further refine the modeling of forms. He was able to indicate contours with a sensitivity that could indicate the swelling and narrowing of muscled legs and suggest shadows convincingly, such as those of the blades of grass (fig. 8).

In comparing Dürer's engraving of *The Oriental Family* of about 1496 (cat. no. 7) with Schongauer's *Two Turks* it is easy to observe how much Dürer had learned from the prints of his predecessor. Dürer delineates his figures as economically and expressively as does Schongauer. The blank paper in the background of each print suggests airy space behind the figures. But, whereas Schongauer's swelling, tapering lines do no more than suggest that his figures have volume, Dürer's lines have begun to explore the solidity of bodies.

It should be noted that those of Dürer's early engravings that show most clearly Schongauer's influence are not as large in format as his other engravings of the period. Moreover, in subject matter and style they must have appealed to a fairly wide public; and possibly it was these smaller prints that Dürer's wife, Agnes, and his mother found most saleable at fairs.

Until the first year or so of the sixteenth century, Dürer was also at work on more ambitious engravings in which he was experimenting with new effects. In *The Prodigal Son amid the Swine* of about 1496 (cat. no. 3), he took pains to represent not only the gross forms of the swine but also the stiffness of the bristles on their backs; not only the farm buildings, but also the dry nature of thatching on their roofs. In the *Four Naked Women* of 1497 (cat. no. 12), he meticulously described the individualized curves of the women's bodies and also attempted to suggest something of the softness of their flesh and the character of the acrid flames of hell at the left. In the *Temptation of the Idler* (cat. no. 13), engraved perhaps a year later, he had mastered the representation of a woman's flesh and by then was suggesting the individual quality of the cloth in the coat worn by the idler.

There is no more demanding form of printmaking than engraving. One needs a high degree of skill in order to incise, ink, and print a plate. In addition, intellectual ability is required to project in advance how deep each line engraved in the metal must be in order to print the precise strength of line desired.

One can see plainly that Dürer needed time to solve such problems. He sometimes failed to calculate how deep certain lines should be. Thus the shading on the left cheek of the Virgin in *The Holy Family with the Butterfly* (cat. no. 2) almost immediately printed too lightly. And he also sometimes had difficulty in wiping the plate; see for example, around Saint Eustace's foot (cat. no. 59). Insufficient wiping may also have caused the tone in the *Young Woman Attacked by Death* (cat. no. 1).

Italianate influences and classical motifs have been noted by art historians in some of his large early prints. But in conception, they are still Northern in spirit. The calligraphic lines of these prints, which are punctuated by strong, dark accents, are printed in a vibrant black ink that forms a dramatic contrast with the white paper. In all of Dürer's early plates, the lines are engraved deeply enough so that they were able to produce good, legible impressions for a surprisingly long time.

By the opening years of the sixteenth century, Dürer had learned not only to represent different textures convincingly but also to exploit even more subtle surface variations. Thus, in the *Saint Eustace* of about 1501 (cat. no. 59), he is able to differentiate between the gleaming hide of a horse and the supple softness of hounds' coats. He was resolving the difficulties of wiping copper plates and was usually able to clean them sufficiently so that all engraved lines would print clearly. His prints are no longer conceived in fifteenth-century terms of vibrant, strong contrasts but in a muted tonality.

Fig. 6. *Mother with Two Children and a Blank Shield,* and *Bearded Man with a Blank Shield,* a pair of drypoints by the Housebook Master (Katherine Eliot Bullard Fund. 66.375 and 66.376)

Fig. 7. *Two Turks,* engraving by Martin Schongauer (George Peabody Gardner Fund. 42.397)

Fig. 8. *Two Turks* (enlarged detail of engraving by Schongauer)

In 1504 Dürer engraved the *Fall of Man* (cat. no. 84), a print of which he was so justly proud that it is the only one to which he signed his name in full. Much has been written about the figures of Adam and Eve; many drawings have been reproduced that were made by Dürer in his search to divine the ideal proportions of human form. His dependence on earlier Italian studies is well known; and the iconographical identities of the denizens Dürer chose to inhabit Eden have been discussed (see Panofsky, vol. 1, pp. 84–87). What should be noted here are the differences between this engraving and the *Saint Eustace.* Where the woods, the animals, and the saint were arranged as in a medieval tapestry, Adam and Eve stand like Greek statues before the shadowed darkness of the forest. But there is also a more subtle and profound difference between the two engravings: strong sunlight has entered into the scene. In early impressions, the modest fig branches cast sharp shadows on the figure's thighs, and the crisp curls of Adam's hair sparkle. From this year until the end of Dürer's life, light will have an active role to play in his prints.

There is probably no engraving in which Dürer explored texture more minutely than in *The Nativity* of 1504, (cat. no. 86). He depicts leafy flourishing bushes, stiff thatching, dried and broken plaster, weathered wood, and glimmering stone in great detail, using extremely fine lines of hatching and cross-hatching. In a print by a lesser artist, this extravagance of detail might appear as an end in itself. But Dürer's sensitivity to the rational ordering of forms within a composition forces every detail into subordination to the whole design. No copper plate in which so many areas of texture have been engraved with such marked delicacy of line can be printed for long without serious distortion of the image. And none of Dürer's engraved plates of the sixteenth century have the hardiness of his fifteenth-century ones.

The *Engraved Passion* (cat. nos. 93–108) was executed during the years 1507–1512. In these plates there is a marked darkening of the whole image, the figures being accented by a restrained, yet expressive, light that comments on the somber events. In the *Fall of Man* of 1504, Adam and Eve, as immobile as statues, stood out boldly against the dark background. In the *Small Passion,* the various soldiers, officials, priests, and Christ and his followers, will lift their arms with emotion, fight, gesticulate, mock, or scourge. But so carefully is each scene designed that a rational order contains the intensity of their actions within the boundaries of the composition.

The printing ink used in these impressions seems to have been of a different consistency than that used in Dürer's early engravings, for example *The Prodigal Son* (cat. no. 3). By 1512, Dürer had begun to experiment with leaving a light film of ink on small areas of the copper plate for expressive reasons. In the impression of the *Ecce Homo* (cat. no. 100), translucent tones of ink give greater emphasis to the majestic, suffering figure of Christ.

In the same year that saw the completion of *The Small Passion,* Dürer tried drypoint for the first time, a medium that the Housebook Master had used. In Dürer's small plate *The Man of Sorrows with Hands Bound* (B. 21, not exhibited), there is nothing in his use of the medium that would differentiate it on technical grounds from a great many drypoints by his predecessor. To all appearances, the Housebook Master did not force his drypoint tool to raise extra burr on the plate. Dürer, on the contrary, in the space of a single year, intuitively grasped the potential of burr in printed impressions.

In the copper plate of *Saint Jerome by the Pollard Willow* of 1512 (cat. no. 175) he used burr, which printed as velvety patches, to describe further the character of such objects as the pollarded tree and the shadowed, silken mane of the lion. He used it, too, to give an airy atmosphere to the landscape similar to the effects in Venetian paintings he had seen a few years earlier. In this exceptionally beautiful impression, the expertness with which Dürer was able to use selective wiping is visible. Here it serves a twofold purpose: to give architectural monumentality to the composition, and to form a union between the softly lit sky and the frail flesh of the saint.

In 1513 and 1514 Dürer engraved three prints that may have been conceived as a group, *Knight, Death, and the Devil* (cat. nos. 179–181), *Saint Jerome in his Study* (cat. nos. 186–187), and *Melencolia I* (cat. nos. 188–189). The most renowned of his prints, they have been admired by collectors, scholars, and amateurs for centuries. The iconographical complexities have been discussed many times. The compositions have been reproduced so often that one might speak of them as monuments of printmaking. But unlike many great works seen too often, misused in various ways, or bowdlerized, these three prints still exert a fascination, provided that they are seen in fresh, early impressions. It is only then that the prints seem alive and that their full strength and beauty can be comprehended.

When the earlier impression of *Saint Jerome in his Study* (cat. no. 186) was printed, the plate was virtually without wear. Every object in the saint's study has the precise balance of light and dark tones intended for it by Dürer. The gourd hanging from the rafters is rounded; the fur of the dog and lion have inherent individual qualities; and the room is filled with translucent shadows and warm light. The saint himself, with his brilliant halo, takes his rightful position as the most important being in the composition. In the second impression of this print (cat. no. 187), good though it is, not a single one of these effects is convincing.

After Dürer's return from Italy in 1507 he began to work larger and larger areas of the surface of his plates until little remained blank. At the same time, he was further narrowing the range of lights and darks in his prints. Where the *Holy Family with the Butterfly* of about 1495 (cat. no. 2) was not unlike a drawing printed in black ink on white paper, the engravings of the later period more nearly resemble monochrome paintings.

Dürer used these self-imposed limitations with great expressiveness. In *Knight, Death, and the Devil* of 1513, the predominently somber tones suggest the mysterious darkness of the vale of death through which the armored Christian knight rides on his gleaming horse. In *Melencolia I* of 1514, the brooding, winged woman, the tools, the hourglass, the landscape, the great geometric shapes are all depicted in quiescent grays without strong contrasts. Two fine impressions of each of these subjects are exhibited. So close are they in quality that in each instance a single impression would have sufficed were it not that a pair shows a characteristic of very early impressions of these subjects and also of the *Saint Jerome in his Study:* they are printed in various inks ranging from blue black to brownish or silvery shades on white or warm yellowish paper.

In 1515, Dürer began to experiment with yet another technique, etching, a medium other craftsmen, notably armorers, had been using, but which printmakers did not explore until the sixteenth century. Dürer, like most of the early German artists, etched on iron or steel plates rather than on copper. His first etching, the *Man of Sorrows* (cat. no. 190), is modest in size and halting and inexpert in execution. Just as Dürer had almost immediately comprehended a new dimension of the drypoint medium, he approached etching with an instinctive inventiveness. In that same year, he executed the highly accomplished *Agony in the Garden* (cat. no. 191). Unlike other German artists who etched in these first years of the century, Dürer never sought to imitate engravings but gave to his etched lines unusual breadth and great calligraphic vigor. His prints in this medium should not be considered in isolation from the rest of the prints executed during the same period. Though he did not imitate engraving, he translated engraving techniques into terms that were suitable to the character of his etched line. In the *Agony in the Garden,* light plays its customary important role, but here it has an inner vitality of its own. Tonal inking is used to darken the shadows behind the figure of

Christ, heightening the brilliance of his cruciform halo and intensifying his isolation and agony.

Dürer's etched plates did not show the same signs of rapid wear as his engraved plates of the same years, probably because of the breadth of the lines and the relative toughness of the iron or steel plates.

From 1519, the year he engraved the *Saint Anthony* (cat. no. 210), Dürer customarily conceived his engravings in a limited range of silvery grays. These late works are his least understood prints. It may be that our opinion of them is colored by our familiarity with a wealth of undistinguished imitators from the sixteenth through the nineteenth centuries who took over Dürer's vocabulary and his narrow tonal range but who lacked both the acuteness of his feeling for balance and his ability to state whatever he wished with great skill and sensitivity. Furthermore, it is only after one has come to know Dürer's late engravings well, that one will not mistake a fine impression for a worn one simply because one is more accustomed to thinking of his work in bolder terms of black and white.

In Dürer's portrait of *Cardinal Albrecht of Brandenburg,* 1523, (cat. no. 215), not only has the range of tonality been reduced to an absolute minimum, but the manner in which he engraves is extremely delicate and almost abstract. In lesser hands, a print engraved with such restrictions could be austere, yet in a fine impression of the Cardinal, there is neither a lessening of radiant light nor of textural description so that translucent shadows play across the bare wall behind him, and his woolen clothing and fleshy face are fully realized. In the closing years of Dürer's life, his prints, restrained though they are in means, possess a cogent beauty and, when warranted by the subject matter, a feeling akin to intimacy. Dürer has turned to using his extraordinary power with singularly gentle skill.

Dürer's Woodblocks

In Germany, in the fifteenth century, woodblock cutting was a specialized craft undertaken by professionals. The designs they followed were by no means always their own. Altar pieces, illuminations in manuscripts, even statues, have been traced as the ultimate source of a number of their designs; they frequently copied other woodcuts. In the German book publishing centers, including Nuremberg, these professionals found ready employment. Arthur M. Hind was of the opinion that Dürer rarely, if ever, cut his own blocks and that the difference in the quality of his woodcuts depended on whether he drew directly on the block or submitted a drawing to a cutter (*An Introduction to a History of Woodcut,* vol. II, Boston and New York, 1935, p. 386). Hind may be correct, though it is doubtful that the history of the cutting of Dürer's blocks throughout his life can ever be fully reconstructed.

The woodblock in Basel for the 1492 *Saint Jerome in his Study* is cut in such a stolid and graceless manner, it would be hard to believe that Dürer, rather than a local craftsman, was the cutter. All his life, even as a child, Dürer strove for perfection in almost everything he did and approached his work with incisiveness and imagination. By the time he left Wolgemut's workshop in 1489, he had outstripped his master.

In contradistinction, the woodblocks for five of the ambitious woodcuts executed from about 1496–1498 — the *Hercules* and *Martyrdom of the Ten Thousand* (cat. nos. 17 and 26), both in the British Museum, London; *Samson Rending the Lion* (cat. no. 24) and the *Martyrdom of Saint Catherine* (not exhibited), both in the Metropolitan Museum, New York; and the *Holy Family with Three Hares* (cat. no. 19) in the Art Museum, Princeton, New Jersey — are extraordinary works of art in themselves. William Ivins suggested that Dürer cut these himself ("Notes on Three Dürer Woodblocks," *Metropolitan Museum Studies,* vol. 2, [1929–1930], 102–111). Whether or not this is true, the blocks have great sculptural beauty and are chiseled, cut, and incised with freedom and con- fidence. In addition, they have been cut with an acute understanding of the woodcut lines as they would print on paper.

If we assume that Ivins' theory concerning these early large blocks is correct and Dürer did cut them, other prints, later blocks, and documentary evidence reveal that this did not remain his method. None of the fifteenth- century woodblocks for the *Apocalypse* and the *Large Passion* have survived, but a study of the earlier *Large Passion* prints suggests that at least two cutters may have worked on the blocks. In the *Deposition* (cat. no. 57) the

printed lines have an uncertainty and clumsiness not apparent in the other subjects in this group. Between 1504 and 1505 Dürer seems to have given eleven designs, including *Saint George on Horseback* (cat. no. 83), to an artisan who cut them with a certain vigor but who was insensitive to any of the linear subtleties of the drawings.

In the nineteenth century, the wood engraver John Thompson observed that at least four separate cutters had been involved between 1509–1511 in producing the *Small Passion* blocks in the British Museum. The blocks display quite different basic approaches to cutting and varying degrees of proficiency ranging from timidity to firmness. These *Small Passion* blocks are totally unlike the five fifteenth-century blocks listed above, having nothing of their lively, sculptural quality and crisp, sure beauty.

Toward the end of his career, Dürer employed the cutter Hieronymus Andreä (Resch), so well known in Nuremberg that he was called Hieronymus Formschneyder (Hieronymus the Cutter). It is certain that Dürer used Andreä and his workshop to cut the blocks for Maximilian's *Triumphal Arch* dated 1515 (cat. no. 204), since his name appears on the backs of the blocks, which are preserved in the Albertina, Vienna. It was also Andreä who was responsible for printing the illustrations in and publishing Dürer's theoretical treatises.

Stylistic Development in Dürer's Woodcuts

When Dürer first began to engrave after his return to Nuremberg from Italy in 1495, he was forced to overcome a number of technical problems. There were, however, no such difficulties apparent in the woodcuts he pro- duced during the five years subsequent to that journey. The *Hercules* of about 1496 (cat. no. 17), is an incredibly accomplished print, ambitious in format and complex in design. He shades the old woman's musculature in great detail and takes pains to render the intricacies of armor and chain mail. It would be hard to cite a comparable fifteenth-century woodcut. A stylistic similarity exists between his prints in the woodcut and engraving media in the closing years of the fifteenth century. They share strong lines and vigorous black accents contrasting with broad areas of blank paper. The white of the paper in- variably plays a descriptive role, whether it be sky, water, landscape, flesh, or fabric, while also acting as a dramatic counterfoil to the bold, black, linear design.

In Dürer's early compositions, woodcut lines, like engraved ones, have a calligraphic force; but in the woodcuts, they tend to have a greater individuality of character. In the *Hercules* woodblock one can see that the quality of the lines has been further varied through great skill and subtley in cutting. As a further refinement, the height of the lines (as they stand in relief from the block) has also been varied to produce in the print delicate, tapering ends to the shading and greater crispness in areas of cross-hatching.

Dürer's *Apocalypse*, illustrating the *Revelations of Saint John*, was revolutionary in its time in both technique and breadth of concept. Never before had a single artist executed a project of such scope with total mastery of every aspect. The fifteen woodcuts completed between 1496 and 1498 vividly explore the natural world and the violent events of Saint John's visions, capturing minute detail, varied textures, a strong sense of movement, and the evocation of light and darkness.

Only in iconography are the prints traditional. Scholars long ago observed Dürer's dependence on the illustrations in the ninth German *Bible*, published in 1483 by his godfather, Anton Koberger. These illustrations had, in turn, been reprinted from the Quentell *Bible* of about 1479.

In general, Dürer adhered with surprising fidelity to scriptural and apocryphal texts and to the accounts brought back from the Holy Land by pilgrims. It may be that he did so not from any leaning toward orthodoxy as an end in itself but, rather, from a drive to reexamine all the basic evidence he could find relevant to any project he undertook.

During these very productive five years at the end of the fifteenth century, Dürer also made seven large woodcuts that he published in 1511, together with a title page and four additional prints, as the *Passion of Christ*. It is interesting that Giorgio Vasari, writing in 1550 on Dürer's *Large Passion*, accepted as genuine only the four more classical scenes cut in 1510. The seven fifteenth-century pieces were, in Vasari's eyes, no more than a crude travesty of Dürer's work produced posthumously to fill out the set. In the earlier group, Dürer was not always successful in presenting well-articulated limbs; but the figures, even in their occasional awkwardness, have an outstanding emotional expressiveness and vitality made possible by Dürer's bold use of the woodcut line.

By the beginning of the sixteenth century, Dürer had mastered every skill necessary for the execution of a successful woodcut. Whether or not Dürer cut his own blocks, he was able to predetermine the printed effect of lines and to achieve seemingly effortless results.

Throughout his life, there are only rare instances when Dürer fell short of technical excellence. Possibly these may be explained by the fact that some craftsmen had difficulties in converting his drawings into woodcuts.

When we confront seventeen scenes from the *Life of the Virgin* of about 1501–1505, it is not difficult to sense that Dürer was wrestling with, and solving, new problems, though not necessarily technical ones. The manner in which the woodcut lines describe forms is similar to that of Dürer's fifteenth-century woodcuts; there is the same brilliant contrast of bold, black lines with ample portions of white paper.

However, in mood, the *Life of the Virgin* is more sedate that any of his earlier woodcuts, due in part to the domestic setting he gave the scenes. Architecture is used to frame and stabilize compositions as well as to establish fluid, continuously receding space as a setting for the activities taking place around the Virgin. As in his engravings of the same years, he goes to great lengths to suggest textural detail. Broad areas of stone and wooden surfaces made unusual demands on the craftsmen who cut them. These areas, hatched and cross-hatched, now occupy great areas of the prints.

After his second trip to Italy, between 1505–1507, his woodcut style changed in a manner that had already occurred in his drawings and engravings. He began to depict form in terms of light and shadow modeling volume, achieving a greater and more classical harmony in his compositions. One can already observe the changes in the *Small Passion* of 1509–1511. By 1510, the difference is striking as one can see by examining a detail of the *Ecce Homo* of 1498 or 1499 (cat. no. 51) and the *Last Supper*, dated 1510 (cat. no. 154, figs. 9, 10). The fifteenth-century detail is characterized by bold outlining of both the gesticulating figure and the folds of his garments. The sparser hatching is executed with lively and very individual strokes. In the 1510 detail, the outlines, more delicate in character, have lost their dominant quality and, indeed, are often blended into the shading, which has a new evenness. In 1498, Dürer indicates dark shadows by increasing the width of hatching and cross-hatching lines. In 1510, he suggests the relative darkness of a tonal area by setting fine lines of hatching and cross-hatching closer together or further apart. These disciplined and regularized lines were to make the exploration of individual textures virtually impossible without sacrificing the harmonious qualities of light and shadow. In the 1510 *Last Supper*, the white of the paper no longer acts as a broad, contrasting backdrop for a black calligraphic design as it does in the *Ecce Homo* but, rather, represents the highlighted portions of a composi-

Fig. 9. Detail of the 1498–99 *Ecce Homo* woodcut, (cat. no. 51)

Fig. 10. Detail of the 1510 *Last Supper* woodcut, (cat. no. 154)

tion in a broad, but calculated range of tones. Dramatic effects are created by the interplay of the white paper with the shaded areas.

By 1511, Dürer succeeded in endowing his woodcuts with many of the qualities he had learned to bring to the medium of engraving. The *Mass of Saint Gregory* (cat. no. 167) is conceived in almost painterly tones interrupted by the startling light that springs from Christ's miraculous appearance on the altar.

By this year, Dürer had either found or trained cutters who could execute his designs with precision and intelligence. Quite possibly it was also easier for them to cut the regular systems of hatching accurately than it had been to follow his earlier, very personal, calligraphic lines. This totally new style of woodcut design was to be developed and refined throughout the rest of his career.

After 1511, Dürer's concern for three dimensionality did not diminish, and he continued using the same technical means for rendering tone. However, in designing the woodcuts that the Emperor Maximilian began to commission in 1512, Dürer was required, by the nature of the subject matter to include in his designs ornate, intricate embellishments and rich textures — the *Triumphal Arch* (cat. no. 204) and the *Triumphal Chariot* (cat. no. 205), are exhibited. Maximilian's commissions, particularly the *Chariot,* are further characterized by lighting that is somewhat theatrical in effect. It is likely that Dürer enjoyed these projects for he had innate gifts for elaborate detail and expressive, calligraphic line. Having evolved the disciplined woodcut style of 1511, he may well have taken pleasure in utilizing for the emperor both his inborn abilities and his hard-won achievements. Even in the *Virgin as Queen of the Angels* of 1518 (cat. no. 206), which was not executed for the emperor, there is still an immense zest for ornament, sparkling light effects, and flowing line, tempered by the systems he had been using to create a painterly woodcut.

In the *Last Supper* of 1523, executed by a cutter of extraordinary skill, Dürer has turned back to a completely tonal composition. As in the portrait of *Cardinal Albrecht of Brandenburg,* engraved that same year (cat. no. 215), the range of tones is extremely narrow, consisting of white highlights and a few shades of gray. One is scarcely aware of the presence of a single black line. It is interesting to compare a detail of the 1523 *Last Supper* with a detail of the Large Passion *Last Supper* of 1510 (figs. 11 and 12). In both prints, the white of the paper serves to suggest various aspects of light: its effect on the surfaces it touches and its ability to permeate various areas. The 1510 *Last Supper,* tonal in conception though it may be, still contains relatively broad areas of sharply contrasting light and

shadow. In 1523 these dramatic effects have been relinquished for simple, broad planes subtly arranged to produce a sense of stillness and grandeur.

Catalogues Concerned with Quality of Dürer's Impressions

Sylvester Rosa Koehler

The great pioneer attempt to set down in writing a judgment on the relative quality of various impressions of Dürer's prints was the work of the first curator of prints of this museum, Sylvester Rosa Koehler. The genesis of his ideas may be found in the catalogue of an exhibition held at the Museum of Fine Arts, Boston in 1888 where both woodcuts and intaglio prints were included. Concentrating on the latter group, Koehler prepared a catalogue for an exhibition of Dürer's engravings, etchings, and drypoints held at the Grolier Club in New York in 1897 (*A Chronological Catalogue of the Engravings, Drypoints, and Etchings of Albert Dürer*).

This catalogue remains an extraordinarily valid work, for Koehler wrote about the fine impressions, borrowed in the United States, in relation to those he had studied in the great print rooms in London, Paris, Dresden, and Berlin. An etcher himself and a friend and patron of contemporary printmakers, Koehler, with his knowledge of technique, was able to correct various misapprehensions of Dürer scholars about how the artist employed the drypoint and etching mediums, and he also proved that Dürer was not the first printmaker to use the latter, as had been claimed. Koehler observed how the composition of printing ink used by Dürer changed as his style of engraving developed and became more tonal. But perhaps the most significant aspect of that Grolier Club exhibition and what must have struck the more naive collectors of Koehler's day forcibly, was his insistence that fine early impressions matter very much. He demonstrated their importance by hanging, side by side for the public to see, impressions of varying quality of the same subject. As he stated in the catalogue, "it is this feature which . . . will enable the visitor to make the comparative study of the methods of printing adopted by Dürer which is quite necessary to the full understanding of the interest offered by these prints . . . As a rule, museums aim only to have one good impression of each print . . . The ideal collection would represent, not only each plate, but also all the various possibilities of each plate . . ." (Koehler, 1897, pp. xlv–xlvi).

Koehler used a sparse number of illustrations in his

Fig. 11. Detail of the 1510 *Last Supper* woodcut, (cat. no. 154)

Fig. 12. Detail of the 1523 *Last Supper* woodcut, (cat. no. 208)

catalogue, supplying his readers instead with written criteria amassed through intently examining prints the whole of his adult life. In *The Holy Family with the Butterfly* of about 1495, for example, he notes that it is only in the very earliest impressions that the Virgin's right cheek is evenly covered with fine shading (cat. no. 2). And he observes that it is absolutely necessary that a fine impression of the *Saint Jerome in His Study* of 1514 be printed delicately so that one is aware of the reflected light filling the holy scholar's room and penetrating into its shadows (cat. no. 186).

Joseph Meder

The most important twentieth-century attempt to set standards for the quality of impressions is Joseph Meder's

Dürer-Katalog, published in 1932. It is a handbook on Dürer's engravings, etchings, and woodcuts, their states, editions, and watermarks. Whereas Koehler's method was basically oriented toward connoisseurship, Meder's was toward science. He determined the general sequence of impressions of every subject by Dürer on the basis of three factors. The first is the condition of the printing surface of the plates and blocks. In the former, he noted the disappearance of the initial burr and traced a history of scratches in the copper that appear and disappear over the years; and, for the latter, a sequence of broken lines, worm holes, and cracks in the woodblocks. The second factor is the color and quantity of ink used and the skill or care employed by various printers. The third is the type of paper they used. Meder reproduced in actual size the identifying watermarks he found in impressions of Dürer's work printed over the course of several centuries. His catalogue is a monumental work, but I do not know of one that is more difficult to use.

The way in which he lists the types of impressions he has seen implies a chronological order that he himself says is not always the case. This is one reason why the sequence of scratches may be easy to grasp as one reads the individual entries but is quite another matter when one tries to apply his comments to an actual print. Furthermore, aside from faint and fleeting polishing scratches, he rarely mentions other more serious ones, which are often found in the earliest and most brilliant impressions, nor does he reproduce these impressions (cat. no. 189).

Meder also fails to warn his readers that it is possible for a scratch to exist in a copper plate but not show up in a print. Thus, in two early impressions of *The Nativity* owned in America (one is cat. no. 86), each with burr, both sides of a long, arched scratch appear on the well head in one impression, while only one side of the scratch is visible in the other. The difference is due to a variation in wiping the plate and has nothing to do with the chronology of the impressions.

There are comparable difficulties in using Meder's sequence of damages to the woodcut blocks. Here, too, he often fails to mention defects that appear to have existed from the beginning. For example, trial proofs of the *Large Passion* title page show the outline of the cloud at the lower right already broken (cat. no. 159). Just as variability in wiping a copper plate can determine whether or not a scratch will show up on a printed impression, the printing of woodblocks has aspects which will determine whether or not an extant crack or small break on the block will be visible in the print. One of these is the consistency of the ink, which may fill in and conceal most of the minor damages to the block. Another factor is the character of the paper. When printing early impressions of the *Apocalypse* that were not intended to receive text on the back, Dürer used relatively fine, smooth paper on which Meder's breaks and cracks show clearly. For the 1498 text edition, a slightly heavier paper was used, but it was not thick enough to keep the typography from showing through on the picture side. For the second edition of this work, printed in 1511 (and for the three additional illustrated books completed that year) Dürer used thicker and slightly rougher papers. These coarser papers may have been selected because they were less expensive; but they also prevented the text from showing through onto the illustration. In these 1511 impressions, the small cracks and breaks, by which one might determine the sequence of printing, are often virtually imperceptible. Indeed, it is

only when one knows in advance the precise positions of defects — within a millimeter — and examines these areas under good magnification that one can find the flaws (cat. nos. 28–29). It is true that in the *Apocalypse* there are additional means by which one can determine the date of the impressions by the makeup of the texts on the verso and by such watermarks as may appear. It is when a Dürer woodcut has neither watermark nor text that one needs to keep firmly in mind how the texture of paper, that common substance, can confuse Meder's system.

There are further hazards, about which Meder is silent, that are involved in determining the earliness of impressions. In the woodcuts, later publishers, quite understandably, often had broken sections of border lines on the block replaced. One must also beware of the printers, dealers, or collectors who all too frequently used brush and black ink to retouch an impression, filling in the gaps caused by splits in the block, the worm holes, and the broken lines (cat. no. 73).

Meder's second criterion — the color of ink and the skill or care employed by the printer — can be extremely useful, provided one has access to a large collection of Dürer's prints in which there are a number of comparable pieces. It is almost impossible, however, to determine whether the ink in a fine, early impression has a grayish, brownish, or black cast unless one has at hand other impressions of equal quality. The degree of skill and care in printing are not absolute but relative. Any impression where these are in question must be compared with others (cat. nos. 188–189).

When possible, Meder ascribed a period to the watermarks by citing their appearance in dated manuscripts and printed books. Where watermarks are found, they can be helpful in dating impressions; but there are many instances where a watermark is a very imprecise guide. Meder conscientiously notes the use of a number of such marks over long periods (cat. nos. 84–85).

The difficulties discussed above illustrate the major drawbacks to Meder's catalogue. But by no means do they constitute grounds for rejecting his work. The physical aspects he ascribes to impressions of varying quality must be taken into account. Yet any evaluation of what is seen should be tempered with a large measure of Koehler's connoisseurship. It is no better to be caught by the snare of objectivity than it is by the snare of subjectivity.

CATALOGUE

The exhibition has two goals: to explore the problem of quality in impressions of Dürer's prints and to provide a broad survey of his development as a printmaker.

The prints exhibited are all selected from the permanent collection of the Museum of Fine Arts, Boston. In order to understand quality one needs to see fine, well-preserved impressions. But their high quality can be fully comprehended only when one compares them with fine impressions poorly preserved or other impressions printed from worn plates and blocks. For this reason a number of less good impressions have been included. In order to provide a broad and balanced survey of Dürer's prints, some fine impressions had to be excluded. A complete listing of the Dürer prints owned by the Museum will be found at the end of the catalogue.

Since the emphasis here is on understanding quality in Dürer's prints, the iconography, or subject, of prints has been discussed only when the authors considered the subject obscure or difficult to interpret. Iconography based on the Old and New Testaments has, in general, not been explained.

For the same reason, there has been no attempt to propose new dates for Dürer's undated prints. Panofsky's dates have been used in such cases. The prints have been arranged in the catalogue in a rough chronological sequence.

For a definition of technical terms such as "burr," "watermark," or "wiping of the plate," see the Glossary. For a general discussion of Dürer's use of printmaking techniques, see the Introduction.

The titles of the prints are based on Panofsky's titles. The prints are identified by Bartsch numbers (for example, B. 92) and described according to Meder's catalogue (for example, Meder 76b). For a discussion of Meder's catalogue system, see the Introduction. The dimensions of the prints are in millimeters. Height precedes width. The reproductions are actual size unless otherwise noted.

The following short titles and abbreviations are used in the catalogue:

Albrecht Dürer	*Albrecht Dürer*, exhibition catalogue, Germanisches Nationalmuseum, Nuremberg, May-August, 1971.
B.	Adam Bartsch, *Le Peintre graveur*, 21 vols., nouvelle edition, Leipzig, 1866, *Dürer*, vol. VII.
Conway	William Martin Conway, *Literary Remains of Albrecht Dürer*, Cambridge, 1889.
Dürer in America	*Dürer in America, His Graphic Work*, exhibition catalogue, National Gallery of Art, Washington, D.C., 1971.
Hind	Arthur M. Hind, *Early Italian Engraving*, 7 vols., London, 1938 and 1948.
Hollstein	*German Engravings, Etchings and Woodcuts ca. 1400–1700*, edited by F. W. H. Hollstein, Amsterdam, 1954–; Vol. VII, *Albrecht and Hans Dürer*, edited by K. G. Boon and R. W. Scheller, [1968].
Lugt	Frits Lugt, *Les Marques de Collections de dessins & d'estampes*, Amsterdam, 1921; Supplement, The Hague, 1956 (for collector's marks).
Meder and M.	Joseph Meder, *Dürer-Katalog*, Vienna, 1932 (M. is used for Meder's watermarks).
Netherlands diary	See Conway.
Panofsky	Erwin Panofsky, *Albrecht Dürer*, 2 vols., Princeton, 1943.
W.	Friedrich Winkler, *Die Zeichnungen Albrecht Dürers*, 4 vols., Berlin 1936–1939 (catalogue of Dürer's drawings).

1

Young Woman Attacked by Death
Probably 1495
Engraving, 115 x 102 mm.
B. 92

Meder 76b
Watermark: Bull's head (M. 62)
Colls.: N. Smith (Lugt 2298), R. Balmanno (Lugt 213),
H. F. Sewall (Lugt 1309)
Harvey D. Parker Collection   P358

This powerful image is engraved vigorously, yet with
sketchy, unsystematic lines. Areas where the engraving is
deep, print as abrupt patches of black, such as on the grassy
bench behind the woman's right leg. This impression is
relatively early and shows traces of burr remaining along
the stronger lines.

Inspired by the breadth and informality of the Housebook Master's drypoints, the style is closely related to
Dürer's early drawings. The Housebook Master's prints,
freely scratched into the copper, inspired Dürer both in
subject matter and style, although Dürer incised his plates
more deeply from the outset. (For a discussion of the
Housebook Master and Dürer see the Introduction.) In his
early engravings, Dürer sometimes chose to leave a considerable amount of burr on the engraved lines, which produced an effect comparable to the Housebook Master's
drypoint lines, although there the burr spreads the ink in
a broader, softer blur.

A gray film of ink, most pronounced in the lower left
corner, is the result of incomplete wiping of the plate. At
the top of the plate, the engraved lines of the fluttering
banderole did not fully discharge their ink, perhaps due to
insufficient pressure during printing.

Representations of Death unexpectedly seizing mortals
were a frequent subject in the late fifteenth century. More
often seen as a skeleton, he is here presented in cadaverous
form.

1. Young Woman Attacked by Death

2. Holy Family with the Butterfly

2a. Holy Family with the Butterfly
(enlarged detail of wash on cheek)

2
Holy Family with the Butterfly
Probably 1495
Engraving, 235 x 184 mm.
B. 44

Meder 42e
Watermark: High crown (M. 26)
Colls.: P. Behaim, 1602 (Lugt 365), H. F. Sewall (Lugt 1309)
Harvey D. Parker Collection   P309

The finest impressions from this plate have the black areas of the deeply engraved shadows more strongly accented, due to the retention of extra ink by burr, as in the *Prodigal Son* (cat. no. 3). In this impression, the burr not only has worn away but the very delicate lines that modeled the right side of the Virgin's face have partially disappeared. This impression, and at least two others, (Fogg Art Museum, Cambridge, and Sterling and Francine Clark Institute, Williamstown) have a pale gray wash brushed onto the right cheek to mask the wear (see detail).

It is probable that this impression was not pulled until close to or just after Dürer's death, if Meder's dating of about 1530–1535 of the watermark in this and the very similar Fogg Museum impression (Knapp Gift) is accepted. If this late dating is accurate, the plate was still in surprisingly good condition. The Museum's impression is lightly foxed (spotted with fungus).

3–5
The Prodigal Son amid the Swine
Probably 1496
Engraving, 246 x 190 mm.
B. 28

3
Meder 28a
Watermark: Imperial orb (M. 56)
Colls.: P. Lely (Lugt 2092), J. Spencer (Lugt 1532)
Seth K. Sweetser Fund   32.537

The originality of this plate is in large part due to Dürer's innovative attempts to suggest in engraving a multitude of textures, such as hog bristles, straw, thatch, brick, and wood. Whereas the blurred lines on the roofs at the extreme left and right might be taken for a printing defect, they are consistent in all impressions and must have been engraved to approximate the fibrous texture of thatch.

This is an early impression of extremely high quality. The deeply engraved outlines of prodigal, swine, and buildings at the right stand up from the paper in sharp ridges of glossy ink, as in fine impressions of Schongauer's prints. (For discussion of Schongauer and Dürer see the Introduction.) Furthermore, in areas such as the tallest tree, the swine's heads, and the hollow of the trough there is ample burr, which retains ink and produces velvety black accents (see detail). The character of fine, early impressions of Dürer's engravings of 1495–1499 depends on these accents. Yet another indication of an early impression is the strength with which the many vertical scratches print. These apparently originated from the initial polishing of the plate and gradually wore away, as can be seen in the following two impressions.

Except for a pronounced horizontal crease across the center, this sheet is in excellent condition. The collector's stamp of Sir Peter Lely, the seventeenth-century English painter, appears at the lower right. Near Dürer's monogram is an inventory number in pen and brown ink (A.g.1.). It was written by the cataloguer who prepared Lely's prints for sale after his death. Both kinds of marks may be seen also on the *Melencolia* (cat. no. 188).

4
Meder 28b
No visible watermark
Coll.: Tomás Harris
Centennial Gift of Landon T. Clay   68.181

3. The Prodigal Son amid the Swine

4. The Prodigal Son amid the Swine

7

3a. The Prodigal Son amid the Swine (enlarged detail, with burr)

4a. The Prodigal Son amid the Swine (enlarged detail, after the disappearance of burr)

Much paler than the preceding, this impression might be mistaken for a late pull from the plate. However, at the time of printing, the plate showed few signs of wear and the lines were still strong. The fragile burr had worn from all lines so that the interior of the lean-to and the inside of the trough no longer printed as opaque black. The shading is still capable of suggesting deep, if transparent, shadows. The tree branches, although still strong and black, have lost the sense of movement visible in the earlier impression where an extra blur of ink was retained by the burr (see detail). The vertical scratches are still deep enough to print clearly, as they no longer can in the following impression, which is on paper with a watermark Meder dates about 1525. It seems plausible, then, that the present impression precedes 1525.

It is interesting to observe that the general effect of this impression is silvery, more limited in tone, and comparable to the plates that Dürer executed after his second Italian journey of 1505–1507. The ink itself is not the glossy black of the previous impression, but it is less oily and grayer. Dürer apparently pulled an up-to-date impression from a plate engraved fifteen years earlier.

A small piece of the lower right corner of the sheet has been replaced and the missing lines drawn in. The plate mark has been strengthened all around with brush and ink.

5
Meder 28b
Watermark: Little jug (M. 158)
Coll.: H. F. Sewall (Lugt 1309)
Harvey D. Parker Collection   P291

In this impression, with a watermark dated about 1525, the vertical scratches discussed in the two previous impressions are barely visible. The plate has worn. It can no longer produce the variety of textures nor the rich dark accents that enliven the early impressions.

5. The Prodigal Son amid the Swine

6. The Galloping Rider

6

The Galloping Rider (The Little Courier)
Toward 1496
Engraving, 110 x 79 mm.
B. 80

Meder 79a–b
No visible watermark
Colls.: A. Alferoff (Lugt 1727), J. Malcolm (Lugt 1489, 1780),
British Museum duplicate (Lugt 305), Tomás Harris
Centennial Gift of Landon T. Clay   68.182

In this and the following four prints Dürer portrayed subjects of every day life. Engraved around 1496–1497, they do
not attempt the complex composition or the careful representation of textures seen in the *Prodigal Son* (cat. nos. 3–5).
However, these small genre subjects are economically engraved with a sense of confidence that is not found consistently in Dürer's large early plates.

   This impression is strong and early; and the deeply
engraved lines, on which some burr remains, stand up
from the surface of the paper with great vigor. The print is
in pristine condition.

7. The Oriental Family

7

The Oriental Family
About 1496
Engraving, 111 x 79 mm.
B. 85

Meder 80c
No visible watermark
Colls.: W. Koller (Lugt 2632), J. Malcolm (Lugt 1489, 1780),
British Museum duplicate (Lugt 305), Tomás Harris
Centennial Gift of Landon T. Clay   68.185

Although most of the burr has worn from the plate, the
lines produced are still very strong and black.

   Turks or other Near Eastern peoples with their exotic
dress were popular subjects with late fifteenth-century
German printmakers, and the prints were often in turn
copied by craftsmen working with other materials. This
engraving was copied in a French tapestry of 1500 to 1525,
which belongs to the Museum of Fine Arts (see A. S.
Cavallo, *Tapestries of Europe and of Colonial Peru
in the Museum of Fine Arts, Boston,* [Boston, 1968],
cat. 17, pl. 17).

8

The Monstrous Sow of Landser

1496
Engraving, 118 x 127 mm.
B. 95

Meder 82b–c
No visible watermark
Colls.: A. C. de Poggi (Lugt 617), H. F. Sewall (Lugt 1309)
Harvey D. Parker Collection   P361

The date of this print is derived from the recorded birth of
such a creature at Landser in 1496. Dürer brings a dignity
and objectivity to the subject, which can be clearly seen
when the plate is still fresh enough to produce strong impressions like the present, well-preserved example.

8. The Monstrous Sow of Landser

9

Young Lady on Horseback and Lansquenet

1496–1497
Engraving, 108 x 77 mm.
B. 82

Meder 84a
Watermark: Bull's head (M. 62)
Colls.: W. Koller (Lugt 2632), J. Malcolm (Lugt 1489, 1780),
British Museum duplicate (Lugt 305), Tomás Harris
Katherine Eliot Bullard Fund   68.200

This is a very fine early impression of a subject Dürer
treated a number of times when he was a young man: a
lady and her lover, here a foot soldier carrying his halberd.
This one, however, is free of the moralizing commentary
made by the presence of the figure of Death often found
in depictions of such subjects.

The heavier lines retain their burr creating black accents, such as on the plume of the lady's hat and on the
horse's trappings. A thread margin has been added to the
left side only.

10

The Cook and His Wife

1496–1497
Engraving, 111 x 80 mm.
B. 84

Meder 85b–c
No visible watermark
Coll.: R. Balmanno, 1829 (Lugt 213), H. F. Sewall (Lugt
1309)
Harvey D. Parker Collection   P348

The somewhat puzzling attributes of cooking utensils
and talking bird refer to a tale that was well known in
Dürer's time: a magpie is whispering to the man that his
greedy wife has eaten the eel he intended to fry for himself. The story appeared in *Der Ritter vom Turn* (Basel,
1493), for which Dürer had designed some of the woodcut
illustrations.

9. Young Lady on Horseback and Lansquenet

10. The Cook and His Wife

11. The Penance of Saint John Chrysostom

11

The Penance of Saint John Chrysostom
About 1497
Engraving, 181 x 118 mm.
B. 63

Meder 54b–c
Watermark: Gothic p (M. 321)
Coll.: H. F. Sewall (Lugt 1309)
Harvey D. Parker Collection   P328

Typical of many of Dürer's early engravings, the print is composed of strong contrasts, not only of tonal values, but also of textures. The dark and craggy rocks of the cave function as a foil for the woman's softly rounded, sunlit figure.

Cut slightly within the plate mark at the top, this impression is nonetheless very fine and retains slight traces of burr in the darkest areas. As a vehicle for portraying the female nude, Dürer chose a late medieval fable attached to the name of one of the Greek fathers of the church, Saint John Chrysostom. A hermit, he fell prey to the charms of an emperor's daughter who had sought shelter in his cave during a storm. His feelings of guilt were so great that he threw the girl over a cliff and vowed to crawl on all fours to expiate his sins. He is seen at the left of the print. Many years later, the girl and her child were discovered miraculously alive and well, and still young.

12

Four Naked Women (The Four Witches)
1497
Engraving, 194 x 136 mm.
B. 75

Meder 69a
No visible watermark
Colls.: J. St. Aubyn (Lugt 1534), Seymour Hayden, V. Mayer (Lugt 2525)
Katherine Eliot Bullard Fund   64.2182

Although the drawing of the three nudes in the foreground is based on observation of nature, their grouping is derived from the antique motif of the Three Graces.

The print, the first to be dated by Dürer, is in a perfect state of preservation with generous margins. Particularly important to its high quality is the fact that there has been no abrasion of the printed surface. Some burr remains to enrich the most deeply engraved lines. The warm color of the paper is most appropriate to the subject matter.

The four women have been identified by some scholars, not as the Graces, but as the goddesses Juno, Minerva, and Venus, with Discordia in the background. Discordia set her fellow goddesses to quarreling when she threw a golden apple among them; and this led to a series of disasters culminating in the Trojan War. Other scholars, however, believe that the nudes are witches preparing for their sabbath. They may be applying magical ointments to their bodies. In either case, death and damnation are indicated by the skull and bone and the devil enveloped in the flames of hell. The letters O.G.H. remain an enigma.

13

**The Temptation of the Idler
(The Dream of the Doctor)**
1497–1498
Engraving, 191 x 123 mm.
B. 76

Meder 70a–b
Watermark: Bull's head (M. 62 or 64)
Coll.: H. F. Sewall (Lugt 1309)
Harvey D. Parker Collection   P340

The pose of the Venus-like nude is reminiscent of those in the *Four Naked Women* (cat. no. 12). But in this slightly later print the parts of the body are connected more organically, and fine lines describe soft flesh more convincingly. Indeed, all surface textures—wooden bench and chest, tile stove, feathers—are described with remarkable explicitness. Dürer's emphasis on surface characteristics, almost to the point of exploitation, was to reach its peak two years later in *Saint Eustace* (cat. no. 59).

The textures read clearly in this strong early impression in which traces of burr remain.

Panofsky has explained the subject matter convincingly by relating it to the German proverb "Idleness is the Devil's pillow." Here, the lazy man dozes comfortably beside his stove, while the devil blows evil thoughts into his ear with a bellows. These thoughts are personified in the naked woman who beckons temptingly to the idler.

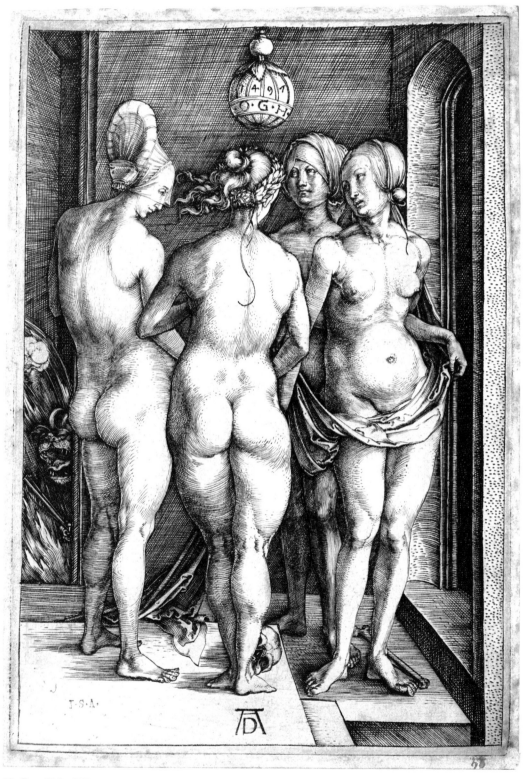

12. Four Naked Women

13. The Temptation of the Idler

14. The Madonna with the Monkey

14

The Madonna with the Monkey
About 1498
Engraving, 191 x 122 mm.
B. 42

Meder 30a
No visible watermark
Colls.: R. Fisher (Lugt 2204), E. G. Kennedy (Lugt 857)
Gift of Miss Ellen T. Bullard   M30789

The figures of the Virgin and Child reflect the classicism of contemporary Italian paintings, which Dürer saw during his first visit to Italy in 1495. In this respect, as well as in a new ability to suggest volume, they form a striking contrast to the mother and child in the *Holy Family with the Butterfly*, engraved about three years earlier (cat. no. 2).

This impression is quite a good one, with clear, strong lines. There are, however, earlier impressions with burr in which forms, such as the large clump of grass to the left, have a stronger three-dimensional effect. In such impressions, the face of the tethered monkey (a symbol of sin subdued) is a sharp, black, compelling mask.

The somewhat hesitant, dry lines in the Virgin's hair are not printing defects, since they are consistent in all impressions, but describe texture, as do the lines of thatching in the *Prodigal Son* (cat. nos. 3–5). Similar lines in the sky may be an early attempt to suggest intermediate tones.

The lower edge of this impression has been cut slightly within the plate mark. Strips of paper on the verso have been added to strengthen the left and bottom margins.

15–16

**The Combat of Virtue and Pleasure
in the Presence of Hercules**
1498–1499
Engraving, 320 x 220 mm.
B. 73

15

Meder 63, II, a
Watermark: High crown (M. 20)
Katherine Eliot Bullard Fund   64.2042

By about 1497 Dürer's style of engraving had altered. Increasingly he had been modifying the abrupt contrasts of black and white characteristic of his earliest prints by the addition of intermediate gray tones, implied by fine lines engraved closely together. This change, which can be seen emerging in the *Four Naked Women* (cat. no. 12) is very evident in the present print, whose principal figures are largely depicted in intermediate tones.

There are Dürer drawings that appear to be based on compositions by Mantegna and a lost figure study by Pollaiuolo, which Dürer may have seen during his first trip to Italy. This print, in turn, is based on the drawings (see Panofsky, vol. I, pp. 35, 41).

The figures, with their carefully observed muscular detail, are arranged before a dark screen of trees, which produces an effect comparable to high relief sculpture. In this very fine impression, it is the blackness of deeply engraved lines with their burr and the clarity of the finer lines of modeling that make the sculptural effect so pronounced.

Tiny blotches are visible in both impressions; see, for example, in the hatching at the lower left and right corners. Similar blotches between lines appear in two impressions of *Knight, Death, and the Devil* (cat. nos. 179 and 180). The apparent cause in both instances is corrosion of the surface of the copper plate. To judge by the superb quality of this impression, the damage to the *Hercules* plate occurred at a very early date.

16

Meder 63, II, b(?)
Watermark: Little jug (M. 158)
Coll.: H. F. Sewall (Lugt 1309)
Harvey D. Parker Collection   P337

The second impression was probably printed in the early 1520's, the date Meder assigns to the watermark. The strong accents of burr and the fine lines have worn away, causing the dark foil of the trees to lighten and the finer details of the musculature to vanish. The figures no longer read as relief sculpture.

15. The Combat of Virtue and Pleasure in the Presence of Hercules

16. The Combat of Virtue and Pleasure in the Presence of Hercules

17
Hercules
About 1496
Woodcut, 390 x 282 mm.
B. 127

Meder 238, I, a
Watermark: Imperial orb (M. 53)
Maria Antoinette Evans Fund   M32606

The *Hercules* is perhaps the most beautiful of the impressions of Dürer's seven large, early, single-sheet woodcuts in the Museum of Fine Arts. The ink is a rich black, and the block has been evenly inked and printed. The generous white areas of the print suggest daylight. They also provide space to contain the violent action and act, at the same time, as a foil for the lines, setting them off so they seem to live and move.

This impression, though otherwise of the highest quality, is marred by extensive repairs, including pen retouching to the left border. The print may have been bound in a book at one time and damaged when it was removed.

Panofsky interprets the subject as Hercules taking revenge on Cacus who had stolen his cattle. Cacus's sister had betrayed her brother to Hercules and is shown being pursued by a naked Fury. The fallen Cacus is represented twice to signify his "duplicitous" character. Perhaps a more plausible explanation is given by Erika Simon in the catalogue of the 1971 Dürer exhibition in Nuremberg, no. 512. She cites as Dürer's source, Pausanius' *Description of Greece,* which recounts how Hercules (who was at war with Augeus of Elis) ambushed and secretly killed the two heroic sons of Actor when they were on their way to represent Augeus at a truce and how Molione, driven to discover the murderer, later exacted her revenge.

An examination of the woodblock in the British Museum, London, shows that a word after *Ercules* was cut away from the scroll at the top. It is a pity, for it might have identified the scene exactly.

18
The Bath House
Probably 1496
Woodcut, 387 x 280 mm.
B. 128

Meder 266b
Watermark: Imperial orb (M. 53)
Coll.: R. Fisher (Lugt 2204)
Bequest of Francis Bullard   M24897

Six men, of different ages and physical types, are depicted in a variety of poses. The musculature of these naked men is treated with the same degree of concern as is the softer female flesh in the engraving *Four Naked Women* (cat. no. 12).

In this woodcut Dürer used a thin white line placed between outer contours and interior shading lines. These "white" lines perform two functions; they accentuate form and suggest reflected lights. They are a device that Dürer also used in his drawings and engravings, as, for example, in the *Four Naked Women.*

This impression is an early one, evenly printed in a strong black ink on a warm toned white paper.

Various interpretations have been proposed for this print: from an erudite iconographical interpretation of the bathers as representations of the Four Humors, to a straightforward acceptance of the print as nothing more than the careful observation of different physical types in an everyday setting. It is generally believed that the figure leaning on the pump is a self-portrait. For a brief summary of these interpretations, with further references, see *Dürer in America,* cat. no. 84.

17. Hercules (reduced)

18. The Bath House (reduced)

19–21

Holy Family with Three Hares

About 1497
Woodcut, 392 x 281 mm.
B. 102

19

Meder 212a
Watermark: Imperial orb (M.53)
Coll.: R. Fisher (Lugt 2204)
Maria Antoinette Evans Fund   M32604

The most delicate shading lines in this fine early impression are still intact. The block, except for the top borderline, has been inked and printed evenly and carefully, so that the printed lines are rich and clear.

The whiteness of the paper and the very black ink of the vigorous lines are characteristic of Dürer's early woodcuts; and these contrasts contribute to a general effect of brilliance, liveliness, and motion within a spacious landscape.

20

Meder 212c(?)
Watermark: Augsburg cup (M. 180)
Harvey D. Parker Collection   P3355

This impression, printed sixty to eighty years after the one above, shows the deterioration that can occur to a block with use and over time. There is a large break in the top borderline, a long crack extends from the lower left border up through the wall, and many other small cracks are scattered throughout the landscape. The lines display the broadening that results from many printings. The closely cross-hatched dark areas have worn and do not print clearly on the coarse paper. Contours that were originally clear are now obscured because they merge with adjacent shading lines, and it is difficult to distinguish one object from another. For example, it is hard to separate the contours of the Christ Child's left arm from the grass, the Virgin's hair, and Joseph's cloak.

Because the details of the figures are no longer easily intelligible, the landscape with its simpler forms takes on more importance. The spaciousness seen in the early impression is lost; and the subtle relationship between the planes of foreground and background is disturbed.

The block had been reworked in a manner similar to that found in cat. nos. 25, 43, and 50. The reworking will be discussed at greater length with regard to *The Beast with Two Horns Like a Lamb* (cat. no. 43).

21

Meder 212i
No visible watermark
Coll.: W. P. Babcock (Lugt 207)
Bequest of William P. Babcock   B116

During the course of two or three hundred years, further wear and damage occurred to the woodblock, and many wormholes, cracks, and breaks are visible. The paper in this eighteenth-century impression has also suffered and is discolored because it has been burnt by exposure to too much sunlight. Although most impressions taken at such a late date come down to us extensively retouched (as cat. no. 23), this sheet does not seem to have been tampered with. Despite being carefully inked and printed, the impression is unattractive and presents only a pale reflection of the original image.

19. Holy Family with Three Hares (reduced)

20. Holy Family with Three Hares (reduced)

21. Holy Family with Three Hares (reduced)

22-23
Knight on Horseback and Lansquenet
About 1497
Woodcut, 390 x 282 mm.
B. 131

22
Meder 265, I
No visible watermark
Coll.: K. von Liphart (Lugt 1687), Tomás Harris
Stephen Bullard Memorial Fund   68.246

As in the *Hercules* woodcut (cat. no. 17) Dürer is depicting
a scene of action, in this instance a knight riding his horse
accompanied by his dog and a soldier on foot. Dürer's
contemporaries were familiar with the curious pose of the
horse and the dog as a convention representing the rapid
movement of animals. A twentieth-century observer, with
an understanding of their movement gained through
photography, cannot accept the convention, yet he too can
sense a motion in these figures which Dürer has given
them by other very subtle means. The strong diagonals of
the lansquenet's halberd and right thigh and the weight
of the dark lines of the bushes behind him give impetus to
the horse; the long curving lines of shading on the ground
below and in front of the horse urge both animals forward.
The trees in the background reflect in various ways the
movement in the foreground.

This impression is early and fine. No impression has
been recorded before the break in the outline of the rock in
the lower right corner.

23
Meder 265, II, c(?)
Watermark: Augsburg arms (similar to M. 178)
Coll.: H. Lempertz (Lugt 1337)
Bequest of Francis Bullard   M24898

At first glance this impression appears to be superior to
the previous one. The outlines of horse, plumes, and
foliage are strong, providing a sharp contrast with the
paper. Since the rock in the lower right corner does not
have a broken outline, one might assume that the print is
an early proof. However, according to Meder's dating of
the watermark, it is an impression printed after 1580, and
it has been completely retouched with pen, brush, and ink.
Most of the printed lines, identifiable by their gray brown
color, have been darkened and broadened with black ink.
The improvements are very deceptive since whoever did
the retouching was sensitive to Dürer's woodcut style.

Nevertheless, in some areas, such as the horse's head and
raised hooves, or the plumes of the lansquenet, the lines
are too broad and draw too much attention. Slight damages
resulting from the folding of the print have been repaired
but are still visible on the horse's neck.

24-25
Samson Rending the Lion
1497-1498
Woodcut, 382 x 278 mm.
B. 2

24
Meder 107a
Watermark: Imperial orb (M. 53)
Bequest of Francis Bullard   M24883a

This is a clear early impression printed on a muted white
paper so that it does not have the sparkling brilliance a
bright white paper would have provided. In this respect,
it is inferior to the *Hercules* woodcut (cat. no. 17) and the
Virgin and Child with Three Hares (cat. no. 19).

The extraordinarily calligraphic character of the lines in
Dürer's early woodcuts is seen throughout, especially in
the lion's shaggy mane, in Samson's hair, and in his
scalloped skirt. Each of the trees on the cliff to the left of
the castle is clearly of a different species, each forming a
distinct ornamental pattern.

25
Electrotype impression, 1920
Gift of the Trustees of the Metropolitan Museum of Art
M28468

The woodblock, made of pearwood, had suffered considerable wear and damage before it was acquired by the
Metropolitan Museum of Art, New York. In an attempt to
make the lines read more clearly, the block had been
reworked; fine grooves were cut alongside many contour
lines which print as narrow white lines. They are
particularly visible in this impression on Samson's right
leg and the lion's mane. A similar reworking, perhaps by
the same person, is discussed at greater length in cat. no. 43.

This electrotype impression was printed by Rudolph
Ruzicka from a metal cast made from a wax impression of
the original woodblock. Many of the major breaks in lines
which had occurred were repaired by soldering and
reengraving of the electrotype plate. Ruzicka used a light

22. Knight on Horseback and Lansquenet (reduced)

23. Knight on Horseback and Lansquenet (reduced)

black ink, paler than that used by Dürer, and a hard, stark, white paper. For Ruzicka's account of his electrotype printing, see *Bulletin of the Metropolitan Museum of Art*, New York, vol. XVI, 1921, pp. 53–55.

As a result of the wear, the reworking of the block, and the use of a metal cast rather than the original woodblock, most of the original clarity and sharpness is lost. The printed lines lack richness and range of value. The hard surface of the paper did not take the ink in the same way as the more absorbent fifteenth-century paper. It is immediately evident that everything appears flat and that neither objects nor figures have volume.

26–27
Martyrdom of the Ten Thousand
About 1498
Woodcut, 390 x 285 mm.
B. 117

26
Meder 218a
Watermark: Imperial orb (M. 53)
Coll.: H. H. Benedict
Stephen Bullard Memorial Fund   65.1024

This is a very black but nevertheless clear impression on a bright white paper of a gruesome subject.

The print represents the torture and martyrdom of ten thousand Christians. In the better known of two separate legends, a company of soldiers commanded by Saint Achatius had gone with the Emperors Hadrian and Antoninus to suppress a rebellion. On the eve of a major battle, the soldiers were converted to Christianity by an angel. The two emperors tried first to torture them into recanting and then crucified them. The less well known legend concerns the torture of a large number of Christians during the reign of Diocletian. Their Bishop Anthimas had his eye bored out with a carpenter's drill; others were thrown amongst thorns. To some extent, as Dürer's woodcut demonstrates, the two legends became fused together.

A decade later, a painting of this subject was commissioned by the Elector, Frederick the Wise, who owned relics of the Ten Thousand. Dürer, using preparatory drawings for the woodcut, completed the new work in 1508, changing the impact of the legend considerably.

27
Meder 218, contemporary copy
Watermark: High crown (M. 21)
Colls.: P. M. Turner, Tomás Harris
Frederick Keppel Memorial Bequest, by sale of duplicate
68.271

This rare contemporary copy might be taken for a poor impression from the original block if there were no opportunity for comparison. If Meder's dating of the watermark as about 1499 to 1502 is correct, this is one of the earliest copies of Dürer's woodcuts. The same watermark is also found on copies of the *Apocalypse,* published by Hieronymus Greff of Strassburg in 1502.

This is a very faithful copy which was probably not intended to be sold fraudulently as Dürer's work since his monogram has been omitted. The slight discoloration of the paper aside, the overall effect is a flattening of the design. The figures have less space in which to move than in Dürer's original, and they lack the organic articulation of his figures. In addition, the copyist has followed late medieval conceptions of the proportions of the body and has overemphasized the heads and facial features. Facial expressions have not always been successfully imitated and are often exaggerated or distorted, as, for example, the face of the man in the foreground at the far left.

The copyist was unable to reproduce the characteristic rhythms of Dürer's woodcut line. Whereas Dürer's woodcut lines have a lively, choppy rhythm that animate the design and make one conscious that the image has been cut in wood with a knife, the lines of the copy are thinner, more uniform, and lack vitality (see details).

24. Samson Rending the Lion (reduced)

25. Samson Rending the Lion, electrotype (reduced)

26. Martyrdom of the Ten Thousand (reduced)

27. Martyrdom of the Ten Thousand, copy (reduced)

26a. Martyrdom of the Ten Thousand (detail, actual size)

27a. Martyrdom of the Ten Thousand, copy (detail, actual size)

28–46

APOCALYPSE

1496–1498 (see cat. no. 166 for title page of about 1511)

Shortly after Dürer returned to Nuremberg from Italy in 1495, he began the preparation of woodcuts to illustrate the last book of the New Testament, the Revelations of Saint John the Divine, or the Apocalypse. It was generally believed that the revelations foretold what events would take place on earth at the Second Coming of Christ.

In 1498 Dürer published both a Latin and German edition comprising a title page and fifteen full-sheet woodcuts, with text printed on the versos of all the cuts except the last. The woodcuts were designed to be looked at independently and do not illustrate the text on the facing page.

Dürer was only one in a long line of artists to depict Saint John's apocalyptic visions. In 1479, Quentell published a Bible in Cologne with somewhat smaller woodcuts illustrating the Apocalypse. These vigorous woodblocks were reprinted in Nuremberg by Dürer's godfather, Anton Koberger, in 1483. Dürer borrowed heavily from them, using both compositions and motifs. But his large woodcuts were unique in their scale, breadth of concept, and unity of design. The woodcuts, except for the first, are a rich but compressed compilation of the saint's prophetic visions. Some depict a single incident, such as the *Vision of the Seven Candlesticks* (cat. no. 30); others combine two or three separate events occurring in different chapters of the Revelations, transcending, as do Saint John's visions, the natural laws of space and time.

Many attempts have been made to establish a chronology for the *Apocalypse* woodcuts. But the lack of surviving preparatory drawings plus the stylistic unity of the set make it difficult to establish the precise sequence. Because of the coherence, comprehensiveness, and unity of the published editions, Dürer must have planned all of the illustrations before cutting any of the blocks. It is doubtful, however, that he designed them in the order they were to appear. In his other series, (such as the *Life of the Virgin*, cat. nos. 63–82, 161–165) one can demonstrate very clearly that this was not his method of working.

Between 1496 and 1499, Dürer's printmaking activity was intense. Single-sheet woodcuts including cat. nos. 17–27, seven of the *Large Passion* subjects (cat. nos. 47–57), and a number of engravings including cat. nos. 1–16, were also executed during these years. Many authorities believe that Dürer cut his own blocks during these three

or four years (see Introduction). By 1498, the *Apocalypse* blocks had been completed and the Latin and German editions issued simultaneously. Dürer was named as artist and publisher on the colophon: "Printed at Nuremberg by Albrecht Dürer, painter, year of our Lord 1498." The Latin text used was Saint Jerome's Vulgate, and the German text was taken from Koberger's 1483 Bible. The type used for the text was one designed by Koberger, but whether he participated in the actual printing is not known.

A number of very fine impressions without text on the back, printed on a thinner, smoother paper than that of the text editions, have survived for about half of the subjects. This paper usually bears the Imperial Orb watermark. In general, the blocks appear to have been in better condition for these impressions than for those from the 1498 text edition. It is, however, difficult to be certain in every case that they are earlier than the impressions with text. The thinner, smoother paper used for these impressions was capable of recording minor breaks and cracks in the block as well as the finest lines; whereas the heavier, more coarse textured paper used for the text editions was not. (See for example, the *Martyrdom of Saint John*, cat. nos. 28–29.) On the basis of their comparative rarity, as well as the high quality of impression and the fineness of the paper, these impressions without text have been designated by Meder as "single printings" (*einzeldrucke*) before the text edition.

For the 1498 edition, a large number of impressions were printed from each block on paper without a watermark. Then the text, in German or Latin, was printed on the backs.

In 1511 Dürer reprinted the *Apocalpyse* with a Latin text and issued it with the *Large Passion* (cat. nos. 47–57, 154–160) and the *Life of the Virgin* (cat. nos. 63–82, 161–165). The new colophon reads: "Printed again in Nuremberg by Albrecht Dürer, Painter, 1511." The three sets were printed on sheets of paper of the same size and quality, usually with the two watermarks, Tower and crown or Flower and triangle. This paper is yet heavier and coarser textured than that used for the 1498 edition. In his Netherlands diary, Dürer referred to the sets collectively as "The Three Large Books." The three series are often found bound together. The inking and printing of the 1511 edition of the *Apocalypse* appears heavier than the 1498 edition, and the text is more visible on the image side of the sheet.

As with almost all of Dürer's woodblocks, the *Apocalypse* blocks were printed throughout the sixteenth century and show marked deterioration. Some were extensively reworked (see *The Beast with Two Horns Like a Lamb,* cat. no.

28. Martyrdom of Saint John (reduced)

29. Martyrdom of Saint John (reduced)

43). However, unlike the other sets for which there are occasional later impressions with careful and sensitive inking, good late impressions of the *Apocalypse* series are not known. Few if any impressions seem to have been taken after the sixteenth century, and it is likely that all the blocks, except that for the title page, were lost or destroyed at that time.

The woodcuts are listed following the sequence of text on the versos, not the order of Bartsch's catalog. The title page, executed about 1511, is discussed in cat. no. 166.

28–29
Martyrdom of Saint John
Probably 1498
From the *Apocalypse*
Woodcut, 392 x 272 mm.
B. 61

28
Meder 164, before the text edition
Watermark: Imperial orb (M. 53)
Coll.: M. J. Perry (Lugt 1880)
Bequest of Francis Bullard   M24883

This is a strong, even impression on warm white paper. No early impression is listed by Meder as being before the break in the top line of the log at the lower right. A second break recorded by him near the top of the right borderline seems to have filled in here with ink during the inking or printing.

This subject is not part of the Revelations of Saint John, but is an event in his life. According to legend, when he refused to worship pagan gods, he was sentenced to be boiled in oil. Miraculously, he emerged unscathed from the ordeal and was set free.

29
Meder 164, 1498 edition with Latin text
No visible watermark
Gift of Edward P. Warren   M9405

The second impression provides an interesting contrast to the first. It is from a complete set of the Latin edition of 1498, which was once bound but had been taken apart before it was acquired by the Museum. It is likely that the set was put together in Dürer's time. All the pages, except the title and the last, are the same size and have large margins. On the versos, the initial letter of each chapter was illuminated in red and blue watercolor, which often bleeds through the paper onto the recto and onto the next page. This occurs here, as well as on cat. nos. 30, 31, 33, 36, 39, 40, 41, 42, 44 and 46. The set was given in 1893 by Edward Warren and will be referred to in the succeeding entries as the Warren set.

The Warren impressions are printed on a fairly heavy, cream colored, somewhat coarse textured paper without watermark, which is characteristic of the 1498 edition. Unlike most of the others in the set, this impression is unusually weak and unattractive. Yet close examination reveals that the condition of the block was no worse than for the above. In fact, here the break in the log is not visible; the line is intact and forms an uninterrupted embossed line on the verso.

The principle defect of this impression is its dryness of printing. A number of technical factors could be responsible for this effect. If paper is not dampened sufficiently to loosen its fibers, the ink will only be absorbed by the surface fibers. When printing ink is exposed to air, it dries and coagulates on the surface of the lines on the block. If pressure during printing is insufficient, the dry ink will not penetrate into the deeper fibers.

30
The Vision of the Seven Candlesticks
Probably 1498
From the *Apocalypse*
Woodcut, 392 x 281 mm.
B. 62

Meder 165, 1498 edition with Latin text
No visible watermark
Gift of Edward P. Warren   M9406

The inking of this impression is characteristic of the 1498 Latin edition as Meder describes it. In several of the Warren impressions, the ink is rather pale in tone, as here. Though the impression is light, it does not lack clarity. A satisfying balance was struck between the amount of ink applied, the dampness of the paper, and the pressure used in printing (contrast to *Martyrdom of Saint John,* cat. no. 29).

30. The Vision of the Seven Candlesticks (reduced)

31

Saint John before God and the Elders
About 1496
From the *Apocalypse*
Woodcut, 392 x 279 mm.
B. 63

Meder 166, 1498 edition with Latin text
No visible watermark
Gift of Edward P. Warren   M9407

This is a heavily inked, strong, clear impression from the Warren set. It is only marred in quality by the red and blue initials and the text showing faintly through from the other side.

32

The Four Horsemen
Probably 1497–1498
From the *Apocalypse*
Woodcut, 392 x 279 mm.
B. 64

Meder 167, before the text edition, b
Watermark: Imperial orb (M. 53)
Coll.: J. H. von Hefner Alteneck (Lugt 1254),
M. J. Perry (Lugt 1880)
Bequest of Francis Bullard   M24884

Meder records two early printings from this block. The earlier is before the vertical crack in the block at the bottom left, which extends from the border to the foot of the Fourth Horseman, Death. This impression was taken after the crack developed. Nevertheless, it is an exceptionally fine impression and has the characteristic strong inking that Meder ascribes to the second group. The watermark occurs on early impressions of the single-sheet woodcuts (cat. nos. 17–19, 24, 26).

The first of the four apocalyptic riders rode forth with the power to conquer; the second, to take peace from the earth; the third, with the scales of justice; the fourth was Death, with hell behind him. Dürer suggests the terrible momentum of the horsemen by various devices: the wind-blown clothing of the riders, the bodies falling before the horses pound across them, and, above all, by the variety of rhythms throughout the complex design.

33–34

The Opening of the Fifth and Sixth Seals
Probably 1497–1498
From the *Apocalypse*
Woodcuts, 392 x 281 mm.
B. 65

33

Meder 168, 1498 edition with Latin text
No visible watermark
Gift of Edward P. Warren   M9409

This impression is similar to *The Vision of the Seven Candlesticks* (cat. no. 30). It is pale but generally clear. However, the areas with dense cross-hatching, for maximum effect, should print more darkly.

34

Meder 168, 1511 edition with Latin text
No visible watermark
Gift of William P. Babcock   B101

The heavily inked 1511 edition of the *Apocalypse* is usually far from attractive. Since the block had already been printed many times, the lines had thickened and the print lacks clarity. For example, the clouds now seem less billowy. When the block was inked for this impression, the ink must have dried out considerably and become less fluid. This has caused it to coagulate in the finely cut areas, such as those in the lower right around the kings of the earth who seek shelter from the falling stars. The text was also heavily inked and is visible through the white spaces of the design.

31. Saint John before God and the Elders (reduced)

32. The Four Horsemen (reduced)

33. The Opening of the Fifth and Sixth Seals (reduced)

34. The Opening of the Fifth and Sixth Seals (reduced)

35. The Four Angels Holding the Winds (reduced)

35

The Four Angels Holding the Winds
Probably 1497–1498
From the *Apocalypse*
Woodcut, 392 x 283 mm.
B. 66

Meder 169, 1498 edition with German text
No visible watermark
Bequest of Francis Bullard   M24886

This impression from the German edition of 1498 was printed about the same time as the Warren Latin edition of the same year. Yet this print produces a different effect from most of the Warren examples. The woodcut lines print with equal clarity but greater strength because here the block had been more heavily inked. The difference would be still more striking had the paper not discolored. The upper right corner, including the breath of the wind, has been patched and restored in brush and ink. The entire left border line is missing and has been drawn in.

36

The Seven Trumpets
Probably about 1496
From the *Apocalypse*
Woodcut, 392 x 279 mm.
B. 68

Meder 170, 1498 edition with Latin text
No visible watermark
Gift of Edward P. Warren   M9411

The ink in this impression seems to be thick in consistency and has collected between the fine lines of hatching on the block, which is visible in the print to the right of the moon and the erupting volcano. Fortunately, this clogging does not greatly disturb the overall clarity of impression.

37–38

The Four Avenging Angels
Probably 1496 (upper section) and 1497–1498 (lower section)
From the *Apocalypse*
Woodcut, 394 x 283 mm.
B. 69

37

Meder 171, 1498 edition with Latin text
No visible watermark
Gift of Edward P. Warren   M9412

The impression is somewhat drily printed in the finely cross-hatched areas of the four fighting angels. Otherwise, this is a clear impression with dark ink.

38

Meder 171, 1511 edition with Latin text
No visible watermark
Bequest of William P. Babcock   B106

As mentioned in the discussion of *The Opening of the Fifth and Sixth Seals* (cat. no. 34), the woodcuts printed for the Latin edition of 1511 are generally inferior in quality to those of the 1498 edition. At first glance, this impression seems to be an exception. The contrast of white paper with rich, black ink produces a brilliant effect, but many of the dark areas are blurred, making their intricacies difficult to discern. Moreover, the outer edges of the image and the contour lines of the four angels print more strongly than the finely cut cross-hatchings, producing an unevenness that disturbs the balance of the composition.

36. The Seven Trumpets (reduced)

37. The Four Avenging Angels (reduced)

51

38. The Four Avenging Angels (reduced)

39
Saint John Devouring the Book
Probably 1498
From the *Apocalypse*
Woodcut, 392 x 281 mm.
B. 70

Meder 172, 1498 edition with Latin text
No visible watermark
Gift of Edward P. Warren   M9413

The quality of this print may be judged on the basis of the relationship between the angel's head encircled by the sun's rays and the figure of Saint John. In fine, carefully inked impressions such as this one, the rays sparkle and dart out from the head of the angel. The delicate sharpness of these lines gives an insubstantial quality to the angel as compared with the heavy contours of the figure of Saint John. This subtle relationship depends directly on how well the lines, as they were originally cut, survive.

40
The Apocalyptic Woman
Probably 1497
From the *Apocalypse*
Woodcut, 392 x 279 mm.
B. 71

Meder 173, 1498 edition with Latin text
No visible watermark
Gift of Edward P. Warren   M9414

This is a good, strong even impression, comparable in its inking to *Saint John before God and the Elders* (cat. no. 31).

41
Saint Michael Fighting the Dragon
Probably 1497
From the *Apocalypse*
Woodcut, 392 x 283 mm.
B. 72

Meder 174, 1498 edition with Latin text
No visible watermark
Gift of Edward P. Warren   M9415

The unevenness of this impression from the Warren set is attributable to an accumulation of ink on the block which clogged the closely cut lines. The result is visible above the hair of the angel at the far left and the upper dragon at the far right. The printing is otherwise of high quality so that the spatial relationship between the rocky foreground and the distant landscape is clearly established. When the lines describing the town begin to thicken, the illusion of distance is destroyed.

A large tear at the top left, through two wings of the angels to the sword handle, has been repaired.

42–43
The Beast with Two Horns Like a Lamb
Probably 1496–1497
From the *Apocalypse*
Woodcut, 390 x 279 mm.
B. 74

42
Meder 175, 1498 edition with Latin text
No visible watermark
Gift of Edward P. Warren   M9416

The heavy dark brown color of the ink in this impression is unlike that in the rest of the Warren set. It is a good impression, evenly inked and printed.

The two brown stains at the bottom right and left of the sheet mar the print's effect. These stains recur in the same places on the three following woodcuts of the Warren set, of which two are exhibited (cat. nos. 44 and 46). From a close examination of the pattern of the stains, it appears that when the book was bound, whatever caused the stains seeped through the pages from the back cover, stopping at this woodcut.

43

Meder 175, after 1511 text edition, reworked block
Watermark: Nuremberg arms (M. 207?)
Colls.: R. Fisher (Lugt 2204), H. S. Theobald (Lugt 1375)
Bequest of Charles Sumner   M21330

There is no text on the verso of this print; and because it is a strong, well-balanced impression, it was once described as being before the text edition. However, Meder dates the watermark in the second half of the sixteenth century. On closer examination, it is obvious that many of the contours, particularly those of the beast with seven heads, have been sharpened and isolated by cutting a narrow groove in the block along the outline, which prints as a white line (see details). It is probable that this was done in an attempt to reduce the broadening of existing lines and heighten their effect. The block for *Samson Rending the Lion* (cat. no. 25), seems to have been reworked in this manner by the same hand, as were the *Holy Family with Three Hares* (cat. nos. 20–21) and the *Flagellation* (cat. no. 50).

44

The Adoration of the Lamb
Probably 1496
From the *Apocalypse*
Woodcut, 392 x 281 mm.
B. 67

Meder 176, 1498 edition with Latin text
No visible watermark
Gift of Edward P. Warren   M9417

The block for this impression seems to have undergone more than average deterioration for the 1498 edition. There is a break in the top borderline, and the composition is unbalanced with a weak center and darker sides. Panofsky believes *The Adoration of the Lamb* to be one of the earliest prints in the series, and Meder records a number of strong, black impressions before the text of this woodcut. Perhaps the number of early printings accounts for the condition of the block by 1498.

   A fold in the paper before printing, which shows as an uneven white crack on the sleeve of the Elder (on the left) who is reaching toward Saint John (in the foreground), and the two brown stains detract further from the quality of the impression.

45

The Babylonian Whore
Probably 1496–1497
From the *Apocalypse*
Woodcut, 392 x 281 mm.
B. 73

Meder 177, before the text edition
Watermark: Imperial orb (M. 53)
Coll.: H. S. Theobald (Lugt 1375)
Bequest of Francis Bullard   M24889

This is an exceptionally fine, strong impression before the text edition. When compared to an impression from the 1498 edition, the block seems to have been in markedly better condition. The quality of the impression is impaired by the loss of the lower right corner from the end of the bank up to the hind foot of the beast. A piece of whiter paper has been joined to the print and the missing portions of the design skillfully drawn in with brush and ink.

46

The Angel with the Key to the Bottomless Pit
Probably 1496–1497
From the *Apocalypse*
Woodcut, 392 x 283 mm.
B. 75

Meder 178, probably Latin edition of 1498
No visible watermark
Gift of Edward P. Warren   M9419

In the preceding illustrations from the *Apocalypse,* it was possible to determine the edition from the content of the text on the back. The verso of the final illustration, however, was blank in both the 1498 and 1511 editions. To determine whether this impression is early or is from one of the two editions with text or was printed after 1511, the paper should first be examined to see whether it is the fine quality of early single printings or whether the sheet bears the watermarks often found in impressions from the 1511 edition or later sixteenth-century printings. In this instance, the paper is identical with the other Warren set prints, and it may be presumed to have been printed in 1498. This supposition is buttressed by the fact that the print is even, legible, and without the later broad-

39. Saint John Devouring the Book (reduced)

40. The Apocalyptic Woman (reduced)

41. Saint Michael Fighting the Dragon (reduced)

42. The Beast with Two Horns Like a Lamb (reduced)

ening of line observed in *The Opening of the Fifth and Sixth Seals* (cat. no. 34).

Its condition, however, is far from perfect. There is a long tear from the right margin to the dragon's head; smaller tears along the left margin; a wormhole near the top in the angel's left wing; and three brown stains, one with a hole in it.

For the title page of 1511, see cat. no. 166.

42a. The Beast with Two Horns Like a Lamb (enlarged detail, before reworking)

43a. The Beast with Two Horns Like a Lamb (enlarged detail, with reworking)

43. The Beast with Two Horns Like a Lamb (reduced)

44. The Adoration of the Lamb (reduced)

45. The Babylonian Whore (reduced)

46. The Angel with the Key to the Bottomless Pit (reduced)

47–57

LARGE PASSION

1497–1499 (see cat. nos. 154–160 for
woodcuts of 1510–1511)

During the two or three years that Dürer was working on
the *Apocalypse* and various single-sheet woodcuts, he also
executed seven woodcuts illustrating scenes from the
Passion of Christ. These last were sold as separate sheets
until 1510, when four more subjects dated that year (see
cat. nos. 154–158) were added to the series. In 1511, a title
page (see cat. nos. 159–160) was designed. Latin verses
were printed on the backs of the illustrations, and the set
was published with the title *Passio domini nostri Jesu*. The
text, drawn from several sources, was supplied by Benedictus Chelidonius (Benedict Schwalbe) who wrote the Latin
texts for two more woodcut books Dürer published in
1511, the *Life of the Virgin* (cat. nos. 63–82, 161–165) and the
Small Passion (cat. nos. 112–152). That same year Dürer also
republished the *Apocalypse* in Latin (cat. nos. 28–46, 166).

Meder identified the various printings of the *Large Passion* woodblocks, and a synopsis of them will be given
here. Since large numbers of single impressions without
text were issued from the blocks, Meder refers to them as
impressions before the text edition rather than as "single
printings," the term he used to describe the comparable
but rarer impressions in the *Apocalypse* (see the introduction to that series).

Both the condition of the blocks and the watermarks
suggested to Meder that there were two separate printings
before the 1511 text edition of the seven early subjects of
1497–1499. The first was printed, as the blocks were completed, on paper with the Imperial Orb watermark that
Dürer had used for the single-sheet woodcuts and for the
earliest *Apocalypse* printings. By the second printing, the
woodblocks had suffered most of the small breaks that are
visible in the 1511 edition, but the impressions are generally more attractive because of the fine quality of paper
used. These impressions before text are, like the 1510 subjects before text, commonly found with one of two watermarks, Monogram of Mary or Bull's Head and Serpent.

By 1511 all of the blocks had undergone some wear, but
the main difference between the 1511 text edition and the
earlier impressions relates to the type of paper used and to
the degree of care taken in inking and printing. With few
exceptions, in 1511 the woodblocks were overinked and
printed on a heavy, coarse paper with the Tower and
Crown or the Flower and Triangle watermarks. The resulting impressions are generally characterized by unevenness

and muddiness. They also have the impressed text showing through on the print surface.

The blocks were printed without text in the course of the
sixteenth century with varying degrees of success. Often
these prints were more attractive than the earlier 1511 impressions because more than routine care was taken with
the printing, no text was printed on the back of the sheets,
and the paper had a smoother, more suitable texture.

By the end of the sixteenth century, the blocks were
probably in Augsburg, for fairly good impressions exist
on paper with the Augsburg Arms, a watermark dated by
Meder between 1580–1600 (see cat. no. 55). Two seventeenth-century printings are recorded—Koppmayer's in
Augsburg in 1675 (see cat. no. 50) and Matthaeus Praetor's
in Ulm in 1690. No subsequent impressions are known.

The *Large Passion*, begun in the fifteenth century and
finished in 1511, has little visual unity. During the decade
that elapsed between the execution of the two parts there
was a dramatic change in Dürer's style. For this reason, the
set has been so divided in the catalogue: cat. nos. 47–57
(1497–1499) and 154–160 (1510–1511).

47

Agony in the Garden
About 1497
From the *Large Passion*
Woodcut, 392 x 277 mm.
B. 6

Meder 115, before the text edition, a
Watermark: Imperial orb (M. 53)
Coll.: Tomás Harris
Stephen Bullard Memorial Fund   68.242

The vertical placement of the main figures in a single
plane in the foreground is a fifteenth-century convention.
There is an abrupt shift to the background where Judas
and the soldiers enter through the gate. A proliferation of
natural detail fills the areas between the figures in a
tapestry-like manner. The animated, expressive lines and
sparkling contrasts of black and white heighten the inherent drama of the event.

This impression before the text edition is fine, early, and
was printed with clarity on paper with the same watermark Dürer used for the earliest *Apocalypse* impressions
and many of the earliest impressions of the large single-
sheet woodcuts.

47. Agony in the Garden (reduced)

48–50

Flagellation of Christ

About 1497
From the *Large Passion*
Woodcut, 382 x 278 mm.
B. 8

48

Meder 117, before the text edition
Watermark: Imperial orb (M. 53)
Coll.: R. Fisher (Lugt 2204)
Bequest of Francis Bullard   M24870

This is an early impression before the text edition. No impressions are known without the breaks in the borderline at the top left. Meder also describes for the earliest impressions a crack which begins at the lower borderline, goes through the dog's left hind leg and back, and continues upward through the right fist of the man seated on the ground. In later impressions, Meder observes that this crack has extended to the top borderline. A close examination of this impression suggests that what Meder saw as an accidental crack was probably a join in the woodblock that was opening up. The very fine line made by the join is easiest to see in the shadows and drapery above the head of the little boy to the right of Christ.

49

Meder 117, 1511 edition with Latin text
No visible watermark
Colls.: H. Marx (Lugt 2816a), Tomás Harris
Bequest of Mrs. Horatio G. Curtis, by sale of duplicates
68.252

The impression from the 1511 editon is basically good, but the letters of the text printed on the back of the sheet intrude onto the blank areas of the design. This causes a flattening of volumes in areas such as Christ's torso and legs. Areas with dense lines of shading, such as between the head of the kneeling soldier and Christ's right calf and foot, lack clarity, not because the woodblock was heavily inked, but because all its lines had lost their original sharpness and became slightly broadened.

50

Meder 117, after 1511, without text, d
Watermark: Augsburg arms (M. 178)
Colls.: G. Storck (Lugt 2318), H. F. Sewall (Lugt 1309)
Harvey D. Parker Collection.   P222

By 1675, the *Large Passion* blocks had come into the possession of the Augsburg publisher, Jacob Koppmayer, who published them with a new title page.

As we have seen, the woodblock for the *Flagellation* had been damaged very early in its history. With usage and time, further damage occurred, consisting of additional breaks in the borderline, a further loss of shading lines in the vaulting at upper left and in Christ's right thigh, and the general broadening of all the lines. The join in the block is visible for its entire length. The complete left borderline had broken off, and Koppmayer inserted a new one. Meder suggests that it was placed slightly higher than the rest of the block, preventing the left side of the composition from printing clearly. It is surprising that Koppmayer did not try to compensate for the poor condition of the block with careful inking and finer paper.

The block had been reworked in a manner similar to the *Holy Family with Three Hares* (cat. no. 20), *Samson* (cat. no. 25) and *The Beast with Two Horns Like a Lamb* (cat. no. 43), but the white lines of the reworking are not as obvious, due to the unevenness of impression.

51

Ecce Homo (Christ Presented to the People)

1498–1499
From the *Large Passion*
Woodcut, 392 x 284 mm.
B. 9

Meder 118, before the text edition, b
No visible watermark
Coll.: H. F. Sewall (Lugt 1309)
Harvey D. Parker Collection   P223

The poor condition of this impression is so distracting that one might first assume it to be a late post-text printing. The sheet is badly discolored and has been mounted down so that it is not possible to determine if it has a watermark. It has been trimmed within the lower borderline; when remounted, the missing line was inked in. There are also two conspicuous stains near the top. Nevertheless the impression is very clear. It is from the second, or later, printing before text that Meder characterizes as having a crack from the lower margin to the hem of the fat man but without other damage visible in the 1511 edition.

48. Flagellation of Christ (reduced)

49. Flagellation of Christ (reduced)

50. Flagellation of Christ (reduced)

51. *Ecce Homo* (reduced)

52–53
Bearing of the Cross
1498–1499
From the *Large Passion*
Woodcut, 384 x 283 mm.
B. 10

52
Meder 119, before the text edition
Watermark: Imperial orb (M. 53)
Coll.: R. Fisher (Lugt 2204)
Bequest of Francis Bullard   M24872

As Meder notes, impressions of the *Bearing of the Cross* printed in the fifteenth century are before any damage had occured to the block. In this example of an early printing, the woodblock was rather heavily inked, which caused areas of densely hatched lines to fill in. There is also a drily printed area from the lowered horse's head, across the waist of the halberdier to the right border. The ink could not properly adhere to this rough area in the paper, which was produced when the damp sheet was hung over a line to dry during the papermaking process. The roughened area actually crosses the whole sheet and can be more clearly seen on the verso.

53
Meder 119, 1511 edition with Latin text, contemporary hand coloring
Watermark: Flower and triangle (M. 127)
Coll.: Earl of Pembroke, Tomás Harris
Gift of the Estate of George R. Nutter, by exchange   68.275

Dürer's prints in black and white suggest coloristic properties so successfully that they did not need coloring. Nevertheless, examples with contemporary hand coloring do exist. It was quite common in the fifteenth century to color woodcuts in books in a rough imitation of illuminated miniatures. Individual woodcuts are also to be found colored so that they resemble panel paintings. It is very unlikely that Dürer colored this woodcut himself. Yet the colors have been applied with extraordinary care and with such great sensitivity to the meaning of the printed image that one is forced to speculate about whether Dürer may not have set the pattern of coloring himself, to be used when customers requested hand-colored impressions.

It should be noted that the highlights have been added in gold, and the metal objects colored with silver. The silver has oxidized and is now gray, making the print less attractive than it was at the time it was colored.

54–55
Crucifixion
1497–1498
From the *Large Passion*
Woodcut, 390 x 279 mm.
B. 11

54
Meder 120, before the text edition, b
Watermark: Bull's head and serpent (M. 81)
Coll.: A. Freiherr von Lanna (Lugt 2773)
Bequest of Francis Bullard   M24873

This clear, even impression belongs to Meder's second group before text, printed just before the 1511 edition. There was by then a fine crack from the lower borderline into the edge of the Virgin's skirt (left foreground).

55
Meder 120, after 1511, b-d
Watermark: Augsburg arms (similar to M. 177)
Coll.: R. Fisher (Lugt 2204)
Bequest of Francis Bullard   M24874

According to the watermark, this impression was printed in Augsburg between 1580–1600. The crack from the bottom borderline through Mary's hem, visible in the previous impression, is here longer and more conspicuous, and there are additional breaks in the borderline. Except for the lines broadened by use, this is a well-balanced and strong impression in good condition. It is remarkably attractive for such a late printing. Great care has been taken to get the most from the block: tonal relationships have been preserved, and there is little loss of clarity.

52. Bearing of the Cross (reduced)

53. Bearing of the Cross (reduced)

54. Crucifixion (reduced)

55. Crucifixion (reduced)

56
Lamentation
About 1498–1499
From the *Large Passion*
Woodcut, 394 x 285 mm.
B. 13

Meder 122, before the text edition, a
Watermark: Imperial orb (M. 53)
Coll.: R. Fisher (Lugt 2204)
Bequest of Francis Bullard   M24876

The *Lamentation* is one of Dürer's most coherently constructed early woodcuts. The tight pyramidal composition
of the figures in a landscape subordinate to them has the
same Italianate feeling as the engraved *Hercules* (cat.
no. 15). This fine, early impression is satisfying in every
respect: in the clarity and balance of inking, in the evenness of impression, and in the freshness of its condition.

57
Deposition of Christ (Entombment)
About 1497
From the *Large Passion*
Woodcut, 384 x 278 mm.
B. 12

Meder 123, before the text edition, a
Watermark: Imperial orb (M. 53)
Bequest of Francis Bullard   M24875

Although Dürer is commonly presumed to have cut his
own blocks before 1500, differences in cutting skill ob-
servable in the seven early subjects of the *Large Passion*
suggest that more than one hand may have been involved
in the cutting of those blocks. A comparison of the
Deposition with the *Agony in the Garden* (cat. no. 47),
executed about the same time, reveals the relative lack of
variety in the lines of the *Deposition*. The lines are generally
thicker and often have blunt, untapered ends, as can be
seen in the shading of the sky. The passages of cross-
hatching are monotonous and less descriptive; see, for
example, the cross-hatched shadows behind Christ.
Figures, such as the man carrying the feet of Christ or the
swooning Virgin at lower right, are less clearly articulated
than those in the *Agony*. The overall effect of this lack of
variety of line and relative clumsiness is less textural
contrast and a reduction in depth.

For the remaining subjects in the *Large Passion*, see cat.
nos. 154–160.

56. Lamentation (reduced)

57. Deposition of Christ (reduced)

58

Witch Riding Backwards on a Goat, Accompanied by Four Putti

1500–1501
Engraving, 115 x 72 mm.
B. 67

Meder 68, I, b
Watermark: Bull's head (M. 62)
Colls.: A. Alferoff (Lugt 1727), D. G. de Arozarena (Lugt 109)
Gift of Miss Ellen T. Bullard   M30790

The *Four Naked Women* (cat. no. 12) accords closely enough with conventional witchcraft imagery that it might have served as an illustration to Jakob Sprenger and Heinrich Kramer's book on witchcraft the *Malleus Maleficorum (Hammer of Witches)*, published about 1486. The *Witch Riding Backwards on a Goat*, however, is both unorthodox and enigmatic in its imagery. Witches were said to ride on the backs of certain animals in the dead of night. Artists contemporary with Dürer show them perched on their steeds with complete disregard for convention. One of the minor crimes ascribed to witches was that they raised storms and damaged the crops of people whom they disliked. In the print Dürer has indicated rain and hail blowing in from the left.

It is the putti, or genii, with their poles, topiary tree, and hollow jar, that make this engraving so enigmatic. They are perhaps based on a poem or emblem that has yet to be identified.

The impression is fine. Arozarena's collector's mark, stamped in blue on the verso, bleeds through the paper and is faintly visible just below the putto seated at the right.

58. Witch Riding Backwards on a Goat, Accompanied by Four Putti

59
Saint Eustace
About 1501
Engraving, 357 x 260 mm.
B. 57

Meder 60b
Watermark: High crown (M. 20)
Colls.: J. Barnard (Lugt 1419), F. Bullard (Lugt 982)
Gift at the request of Miss Ellen T. Bullard   59.803

Dürer was fascinated by the natural world in all its aspects.
The *Saint Eustace*, the largest of his engravings, is a mani-
fest record of his drive to depict nature with an accuracy
almost scientific in its intensity.

The characteristic shape and texture of dog, horse, or
deer, foliage, water, stone, or pebble are meticulously
represented by numerous combinations of engraved lines
or flicks. Covering the entire plate with these closely observed nature studies, Dürer produces a tapestry-like effect,
for the individual parts are not yet integrated into the more
cohesive vision that appears with *The Fall of Man*, 1504,
(cat. no. 84).

Among the profusion of detail one tends to overlook the
subject. While out hunting with his falcon (barely visible
high between the trees diving at its prey), the pagan
Eustace saw a miraculous apparition of the Crucifix between the horns of a stag, and he was converted to
Christianity.

This is a very fine impression, not as dark and fully
inked as it can be, but silvery black in color and printed
with great clarity of detail.

60
Nemesis (The Great Fortune)
1501–1502
Engraving, 333 x 229 mm.
B. 77

Meder 72, I, b
Watermark: High crown (M. 20)
1951 Purchase Fund   54.577

Dürer referred to this print by the title *Nemesis* in his
Netherlands diary. Panofsky identified the literary source
for the imagery (vol. I, p. 81) as "a Latin poem of Politian
which synthesizes the classical goddess of retribution with
fickle Fortune: clad in a white mantle, she hovers in the
void, tearing the air with strident wings, driven hither
and thither by the gales, and always wielding the goblet
and the bridle—symbols of favor and castigation—with a
contemptuous smile."

The landscape, which can be identified as a view of the
Tyrolese town of Chiuso, has been naturalistically treated
by Dürer, whereas the figure has been constructed according to ideals of artificial beauty. Her forms are in part
based on the sphere. The solidity of her body makes one
skeptical of its ability to fly.

The impression is one of a small number printed before
a heavy, accidental scratch appeared beneath the bridge,
which must have occurred shortly after the plate was engraved because of the high quality of some impressions
with the scratch. In these early impressions, the fine details
of the landscape have a crystalline quality, and the burr
remaining on the goddess' wings enhances their texture.

This print is in good condition and has unusually generous margins. The plate mark has, however, been strengthened by tracing over it with a stylus so that it seems to
make a stronger indentation in the paper.

59. Saint Eustace (reduced)

60. Nemesis (reduced)

82

61
Madonna on a Grassy Bench

1503
Engraving, 114 x 71 mm.
B. 34

Meder 31a
No visible watermark
Katherine Eliot Bullard Fund   1971.70

The subject of the Virgin and Child seated alone out of
doors in an enclosed garden is a traditional one. Of
Dürer's many versions of the Madonna and Child, this
engraving and the woodcut *Virgin Mary Roundel* (cat. no.
201) are among the smallest and most intimate. In both, his
chief concern was the warm and human relationship
between mother and child.

A translucent film of ink remained on the lower foreground and around the thorny bush at the fence corner
when the plate was printed. This film of ink, although
probably unintentional, adds to the sense of color. This is
an early impression in fine condition, with the exception
of a few areas in the sky where the paper is rubbed.

61. Madonna on a Grassy Bench

62. Coat-of-Arms of Death

62

Coat-of-Arms of Death

1503
Engraving, 223 x 160 mm.
B. 101

Meder 98b
No visible watermark
Colls.: R. Fisher (Lugt 2204), F. Bullard (Lugt 982)
Gift of William Norton Bullard   M29853

By the age of thirty-two, Dürer had acquired an extraordinary virtuosity in the use of the engraver's burin. The full
extent of his mastery is visible only in unusually fine impressions such as this one, for only they are capable of
doing justice to the marvelous sequence of textures
described. Note, for example, the shining steel of the
helmet juxtaposed to the flowing scalloped cloth of its
mantling. The subtle manipulation of highlights and
shadows on the young woman's dress evokes a feeling of
three dimensionality, which in later impressions is less
pronounced as the plate wears. This very fine impression
thus presents the viewer with a contrast between the traditional two-dimensional qualities of a heraldic symbol
and the sculptural relief Dürer has given it here.

The mystery of love and death, a recurrent theme in
Dürer's early work is here fully expressed in heraldic
guise. A wild man, supporting a shield that displays a
skull, accosts a young woman dressed in Nuremberg dance
costume and bridal crown. The image is a medieval allu-
sion to death similar to that in the *Young Woman Attacked
by Death* (cat. no. 1).

63-82
LIFE OF THE VIRGIN
1500–1505 (see also cat. nos. 161–165 for woodcuts of 1510–1511)

The third of Dürer's "Three Large Books" to be considered here is the *Life of the Virgin*. When it was published in 1511, it consisted of a title page and nineteen large woodcuts. As in the *Apocalypse* (cat. nos. 28–46, 166) and the *Large Passion,* (cat. nos. 47–57, 154–160) the text was printed on the versos of the prints. Benedictus Chelidonius composed Latin verses that served to explain the various scenes from the Virgin's life.

Dürer did not execute the prints in the sequence in which they were bound. The earliest woodcuts in the series were probably executed about 1500, and seventeen of them had been completed by 1505, when Dürer left Nuremberg on his second journey to Venice. One, *Joachim and Anna Meeting at the Golden Gate* (cat. no. 66), is dated 1504. However, concrete evidence for the completion of the seventeen woodcuts before his departure is provided by the existence of copies, two of them dated 1506, engraved by the Italian printmaker Marcantonio Raimondi.

In 1510, Dürer completed the series with the *Death of the Virgin* (cat. no. 161) and the *Assumption and Coronation* (cat. nos. 162 and 163). By 1511, the *Madonna on the Crescent* had been designed for the title page (cat. nos. 164 and 165).

There is great stylistic diversity among the woodcuts owing to the long span of time during which they were created. They are, however, unified by format and subject matter.

Many of the blocks were executed long before the 1511 text edition, and a number of impressions were printed from them before the text was added. These, like similar impressions from the *Large Passion* blocks, will be referred to here as impressions before the text edition. In 1930, the Museum purchased a complete set of them with money provided by the Maria Antoinette Evans Fund (cat. nos. 63, 64, 66, 68, 69, 71–82, 161, 162, 164). These Evans impressions are extremely strong and clear and are printed with a very black ink. The paper is of the highest quality and very responsive to each fine detail and nuance of the woodcut line. The brilliant whiteness of the paper is not, however, merely the result of careful preservation; all of these impressions have at some time been cleaned.

The paper used for the 1511 edition, as well as that used the same year for the *Apocalypse* and the *Large Passion,* was coarser, rough textured, and less receptive to the finer woodcut lines. The imprint of the text on the back is often visible on the image side. In comparison to the clarity of the Evans impressions, the 1511 impressions are generally uneven.

Meder has established, on the basis of watermarks, that there were eight to ten printings following the 1511 publication in the course of the sixteenth century. The quality of these later printings varies with the degree of preservation of the woodblocks, the excellence of the paper, and the care taken with the printing. A printer sensitive to Dürer's intentions was able to obtain satisfactory results in spite of wear or breaks in the blocks; for example, those on paper with the Arms of Würtemberg watermark, which Meder dates about 1580–1590, are quite well printed (see cat. no. 163).

The first seventeen woodcuts of the *Life of the Virgin* are more intimate, more anecdotal in conception than the *Apocalypse* or the early prints from the *Large Passion*. The prints of the Virgin's life are often appropriately domestic in their point of view.

During these years (1500–1505), Dürer was mastering the Renaissance science of linear perspective; this interest is reflected in the varied and very inventive architecture that provides a frame or a setting for the action.

Dürer pushed the woodcut medium to the limits of its ability to describe a multitude of textures and to suggest color. These prints testify to the extraordinary skill of the professional cutters who carried out Dürer's ideas.

63
Rejection of Joachim's Offering
Probably 1504–1505
From the *Life of the Virgin*
Woodcut, 290 x 209 mm.
B. 77

Meder 189, before the text edition
Watermark: Scales in circle (M. 169)
Maria Antoinette Evans Fund   M32073

The New Testament gave very few details concerning Mary and Joseph and the Nativity. To answer the many questions raised by the narratives and to satisfy the thirst of Christians for further details, other accounts were written and interwoven with the events as narrated in the Gospels. *The Book of James,* dating in part from the second century and once attributed to the Apostle himself, gave the history

63. Rejection of Joachim's Offering (reduced)

64. Joachim and the Angel (reduced)

65. MARCANTONIO RAIMONDI, Joachim and the Angel, engraved copy (reduced)

of the Virgin's parents, her birth, upbringing, and betrothal to Joseph. A second very early apocryphal book, the *Gospel of Thomas,* described the childhood of Jesus.

Although Saint Jerome condemned both texts, much of their substance had become deeply rooted among Christians. In the eighth or ninth century these two books were combined and rewritten as the *Liber de Infantia,* or *Book of the Infancy.* It was then alleged to have been written by Saint Matthew, the author of one of the New Testament Gospels. The new version was sanctioned by the Church and was familiar to Dürer.

The first three prints in the *Life of the Virgin* are scenes from the life of Mary's parents, Joachim and Anna. Joachim, a godly, charitable man, went to present his offering in the temple. Here, the priest, Ruben, rejects the offering on the grounds that Joachim must have sinned because his long marriage was childless.

Although this is a very good impression before the text edition, rather heavy inking tends to give equal value to background and foreground forms, reducing the already shallow space of the composition. The closely cross-hatched areas of shadow have filled in with ink and are less transparent than intended.

64-65

Joachim and the Angel

Probably 1504
From the *Life of the Virgin*
Woodcut, 298 x 210 mm.
B. 78

64

Meder 190, before the text edition
Watermark: High crown (M. 20)
Maria Antoinette Evans Fund   M32074

Because his offering was rejected, Joachim was ashamed to return home and went off to the mountains for five months with his flocks. An angel appeared informing him that his wife, Anna, would bear a child. Here, Dürer has given this proclamation tangible form as an official document hung with seals.

Considerable pressure must have been used in printing this very fine impression because the sharp woodcut lines of the tree branch, upper right, have sunk deeply into the paper and raised up a welt of paper around them.

65

MARCANTONIO RAIMONDI
Italian, circa 1480–circa 1530
Copy after Dürer, B. 78
Engraving, 295 x 210 mm.
B. 622
Coll.: H. F. Sewall (Lugt 1309)
Harvey D. Parker Fund   P1293

Giorgio Vasari (1511–1574) states that when Dürer was in Venice he complained to the Council against Marcantonio Raimondi for having made engraved copies of the *Life of the Virgin* woodcuts and using Dürer's monogram. The matter was settled with the decision that Marcantonio should thereafter be allowed to make copies but would be required to sign them himself; and, in fact, he did so on his copy of the *Glorification of the Virgin.*

In the engraved copy the regular, curving burin strokes are more uniform than Dürer's woodcut lines with their lively, angular profiles. He has translated Dürer's linear woodcut style into broad tonal relationships created by parallel shading strokes engraved closely together. This tonal style of printmaking is very close to what Dürer would employ in his woodcuts of 1510 or 1511, such as the *Death of the Virgin* (cat. no. 161) and the *Assumption and Coronation* (cat. no. 162). In the copy, textures are no longer specific; see, for example, the mechanical stylization of the foliage of the tree behind the angel.

Marcantonio's composition is static, and he has simplified Dürer's woodcut by omitting details, such as the birds in the sky or the foremost boat. Marcantonio indicated the location of various elements of the design by sketchy scratches on the plate, which served as a guide when he engraved. One can see that details such as the boat were noted but not finally engraved.

66. Joachim and Anna Meeting at the Golden Gate (reduced)

67. Birth of the Virgin (reduced)

66

Joachim and Anna Meeting at the Golden Gate
Dated 1504
From the *Life of the Virgin*
Woodcut, 293 x 207 mm.
B. 79

Meder 191, before the text edition, b
Watermark: High crown (M. 20)
Maria Antoinette Evans Fund   M32075

Anna was told by an angel to go to the Golden Gate of the temple to meet Joachim on his return from five months in the mountains. Here their reunion is framed by an arched gateway ornamented with intertwining branches on which various Old Testament figures stand.

In this woodcut, the same attention has been paid to rational perspective construction and description of texture as in the engraved *Nativity*, also dated 1504 (cat. no.86). The very specific characterization of textures made great demands on the cutter as may be seen in the fine, irregular lines required to describe the brickwork of the background.

67–68

Birth of the Virgin
Probably 1503–1504
From the *Life of the Virgin*
Woodcut, 295 x 210 mm.
B. 80

67

Meder 192, before the text edition, a
Watermark: Bull's head (M. 62)
Coll.: Tomás Harris
Centennial Gift of Landon T. Clay   68.194

Here, an angel swings his censer as Mary, newly born to her elderly parents, is washed by an attendant woman.

This is an example of an early impression that could deceive a collector owing to its poor condition. It has the characteristics that Meder describes for the very earliest impressions. A wormhole in the drapery of the shoulder of the seated woman at the far left has not yet appeared, nor has the fine crack that extends from the bottom borderline to the framing arch. Although the lines are well printed, the overall appearance is dull and gray; the paper is soiled, there are some thin spots, and numerous repairs have been made. This print should be compared with the late, discolored impression of the *Assumption and Coronation* of about 1580–1590 (cat. no. 163). Both lack luminosity and show how necessary it is to scrutinize the printed lines for evidence of the time of printing.

68

Meder 192, before the text edition, b
Watermark: Scales in circle (M. 169)
Maria Antoinette Evans Fund   M32076

This is a fine, clear impression except for a few uneven passages, such as the skirt of the woman at the far left. There is now a wormhole in her shoulder, and the fine vertical crack from the borderline beneath her through the window to the framing arch has emerged. The latter is perhaps a join in the block which was beginning to widen. Although far more satisfying due to its fine condition, this impression is a slightly later printing than the previous rare early example.

69–70

Presentation of the Virgin in the Temple
Probably 1503–1504
From the *Life of the Virgin*
Woodcut, 296 x 210 mm.
B. 81

69

Meder 193, before the text edition, a
Watermark: High crown (M. 20)
Maria Antoinette Evans Fund   M32077

When Mary was three, Joachim and Anna gave their daughter into the keeping of the priests, and, unaccompanied, she climbed the fifteen steps into the temple. Although Dürer usually adhered closely to written tradition in his religious prints, here he was not meticulous with respect to the details of Mary's age or the number of steps.

In this print, Mary is shown eagerly racing up the temple stairs, scarcely noticeable between the group of figures at the right and the column at the center. Figures, architecture, and perspective are not fully coordinated.

The slightly heavy inking of this fine impression has filled in the densely cross-hatched areas.

68. Birth of the Virgin (reduced)

69. Presentation of the Virgin in the Temple (reduced)

70

Meder 193, 1511 edition with Latin text
Watermark: Flower and triangle (M. 127)
Coll.: Tomás Harris
Katherine E. Bullard Fund   68.218

Seven or eight years later, the block was printed for the 1511 edition. This impression shows evidence of worm-holes, breaks in the borderline, thickening lines, and other damages that had occurred to the block since its creation. Whether owing to wear or to less skillfull inking and print-ing or to all three, the areas of cross-hatching in the print have lost their clarity. The coarser paper and relatively uneven printing are characteristic of the mass-produced 1511 editions. The printed text on the verso is not visible on the image side of the sheet as it often is in the 1511 editions.

71

Betrothal of the Virgin
Probably 1504–1505
From the *Life of the Virgin*
Woodcut, 295 x 207 mm.
B. 82

Meder 194, before the text edition
Watermark: High crown (M. 20)
Maria Antoinette Evans Fund   M32078

Since Mary had vowed perpetual virginity and was at an age to leave the temple, the high priest looked for a man who would protect her and be her husband in name only. An elderly carpenter, Joseph, whose wife had died was chosen through a miracle and betrothed to her.

The figure of the woman at the right with the great winged headdress is based on a watercolor drawing of 1500, in the Albertina, Vienna, inscribed by Dürer: "so does one go to church in Nuremberg" (W. 224).

Although a little heavily inked, the full scale of tonal values is conveyed by this fine impression, and there is a deep and continuous recession into the interior space of the temple.

72

Annunciation
Probably 1502–1503
From the *Life of the Virgin*
Woodcut, 297 x 211 mm.
B. 83

Meder 195, before the text edition, b
Watermark: High crown (M. 20)
Maria Antoinette Evans Fund   M32079

For this woodcut and the six that follow it, Dürer's primary sources were the Gospels of Saint Matthew and of Saint Luke. However, there are often details that are drawn from much later literary sources. Here, for example, in the uppermost roundel there is a relief of an Old Testament heroine, Judith, holding the head of her enemy, Holo-fernes. Her presence was understood in the sixteenth century as a prefiguration of the triumph of the Virgin over the Devil, who is seen with a badger-like face chained beneath the stairs.

In this fine, well-balanced impression, one is fully aware of the print's pale silvery tonality. The choice of this tonality with its feeling of light is most appropriate to the traditional imagery of the Annunciation and is also ex-tremely successful in evoking the texture and color of stone. The more limited tonal range and the extensive use of shading lines are forerunners of Dürer's woodcut style of 1510–1511.

A break in the borderline and scratches in the shading immediately above the borderline in the area below the angel's left foot have been drawn in with ink.

70. Presentation of the Virgin in the Temple (reduced)

71. Betrothal of the Virgin (reduced)

72. Annunciation (reduced)

73. Visitation (reduced)

73
Visitation
Probably 1504
From the *Life of the Virgin*
Woodcut, 299 x 210 mm.
B. 84

Meder 196, before the text edition
Watermark: High crown (M. 20)
Maria Antoinette Evans Fund   M32080

Very strong and clear, this is one of the finest Evans impressions before the text edition. An impression of such quality, reveals how effectively Dürer used the white of the paper to suggest the radiance of sunlight in the mountainous landscape background. This is achieved, in part, through the contrast provided by the darkening of the sky and the dark line of trees in the middle distance.

At first glance, this appears to be an impression printed before two vertical splits in the block above the clouds that Meder describes as having occurred in fine early impressions. However, upon closer examination with the aid of magnification, it is evident that these losses have been skillfully touched in with pen and ink.

74
Nativity
Probably 1502–1503
From the *Life of the Virgin*
Woodcut, 296 x 208 mm.
B. 85

Meder 197, before the text edition, b
Watermark: Scales in circle (M. 169)
Maria Antoinette Evans Fund   M32081

In the woodcuts from the *Life of the Virgin* executed by 1505, the angle of the perspective sometimes leads one's attention away from the principal figures, in this instance, the Virgin and Child. Nevertheless, light areas in the architectural setting, such as the broken wall at left, the gaping hole in the roof, the open arch, all join with the shepherds, the Holy Family, and the angels to form an oval pattern that binds the composition together.

This is a fine impression; a few small breaks in the upper border have been drawn in with ink.

75
Circumcision
Probably 1505
From the *Life of the Virgin*
Woodcut, 292 x 210 mm.
B. 86

Meder 198, before the text edition, a-b
Watermark: High crown (M. 20)
Maria Antoinette Evans Fund   M32082

To the right of the crowd of figures attending the circumcision of the infant Jesus stands the mournful Virgin, her hands folded in prayer. Counterbalancing her is a solitary figure with a candle. The elaborate, braided candlestick directs one's attention upward to the twining tracery above the arched doorway. Among its branches stand the figures of Moses and Judith, seen respectively in *Joachim and Anna Meeting at the Golden Gate* (cat. no. 66) and the *Annunciation* (cat. no. 72).

This is a clear and strong impression, and, as each of the Evans set, it is beautifully preserved.

74. Nativity (reduced)

75. Circumcision (reduced)

76

Adoration of the Magi

1503

From the *Life of the Virgin*

Woodcut, 296 x 209 mm.

B. 87

Meder 199, before the text edition, b
Watermark: Scales in circle (M. 169)
Maria Antoinette Evans Fund   M32083

Pilgrims returning from the Holy Land frequently reported that a ruined castle was the site where the Adoration of the Magi took place. Brother Felix Fabri, from Ulm, who went to Bethlehem about 1481, wrote that long before Jesus' birth, the castle had fallen into ruins. A hovel was attached to one end of the broken wall and was used by the poor as an inn for themselves and their cattle. It was there, he says, that Mary and Joseph took refuge.

Dürer, in his representation of the castle, took pains to suggest the multitude of contrasting textures: thatch, wood, stone, and a variety of plant life. The composition is also full of anecdotal detail, such as the ass who gazes up at the caroling angels in the sky.

This is a fine impression, although many of the lines in the blackest areas meld together and produce sharper contrasts than were probably intended.

77

Presentation of Christ

Probably 1505

From the *Life of the Virgin*

Woodcut, 296 x 210 mm.

B. 88

Meder 200, before the text edition
Watermark: High crown (M. 20)
Maria Antoinette Evans Fund   M32084

The imaginative architectural setting, with its ponderous beams and massive columns, adds solemnity to the event portrayed, the presentation of the infant Jesus in the temple of Jerusalem. The parallel shading lines produce gray tones that suggest a subdued lighting. The extensive use of such a system of parallel lines in this print predicts Dürer's new woodcut style of 1510–1511.

The continuous extension of space into the shadows of the background is very effective in this impression owing to the clarity of the fine cross-hatching.

78

Flight into Egypt

Probably 1504

From the *Life of the Virgin*

Woodcut, 295 x 209 mm.

B. 89

Meder 201, before the text edition, b-c
Watermark: Scales in circle (M. 169)
Maria Antoinette Evans Fund   M32085

The prominence in this print of the stately date palm at the left is explained by a traditional literary and artistic motif associated with the Flight into Egypt. The *Book of the Infancy* relates that when the Virgin wished to eat some of the fruit, the tree bowed down to her. The form of the date palm and the other exotic tree behind Joseph were adapted from Schongauer's engraving of this subject (B. 7) in which small angels help to bend the tree. The subject gave Dürer the opportunity to create one of his most beautiful landscapes. There is a great profusion and variety of vegetation, and the wood is inhabited by a stag and rabbit glimpsed between the trees in the distance.

This is a fine impression, brilliantly printed, that suggests a rich, painterly surface. A small flaw above the uppermost cluster of dates in the palm tree has been filled in with ink.

76. Adoration of the Magi (reduced)

77. Presentation of Christ (reduced)

78. Flight into Egypt (reduced)

79. Sojourn of the Holy Family in Egypt (reduced)

79
Sojourn of the Holy Family in Egypt
About 1501–1502
From the *Life of the Virgin*
Woodcut, 298 x 209 mm.
B. 90

Meder 202, before the text edition, b
Watermark: Scales in circle (M. 169)
Maria Antoinette Evans Fund   (M32086)

Panofsky suggests that this woodcut and the *Glorification of the Virgin* (cat. no. 82) were originally conceived as single devotional images and only later incorporated into the *Life of the Virgin*. In such a devotional image, the presence of God the Father and the Holy Ghost in the form of a dove were traditional and were used by Dürer in his engraving of the *Holy Family with a Butterfly* (cat. no. 2) of about 1495. If Dürer's intention had been simply to represent the daily tasks performed in Egypt by Joseph and Mary, the august attendance of God and the Holy Ghost would be inappropriate.

This lightly inked impression enables the details of the print to be read more clearly than many of the Evans impressions.

80
Christ among the Doctors
Probably 1503–1504
From the *Life of the Virgin*
Woodcut, 295 x 208 mm.
B. 91

Meder 203, before the text edition
Watermark: High crown (M. 20)
Maria Antoinette Evans Fund   M32087

The viewer must work his way through the group of learned doctors in order to find the figure of the young Christ at the lectern questioning the teachers in the temple.

This impression has been carefully printed so that the fine shading lines are clearly legible. A small break in the center of the lower borderline beneath the foot of the standing figure, which appears in the earliest impressions, has been filled in with ink.

81
Christ Taking Leave from His Mother
Probably 1503–1504
From the *Life of the Virgin*
Woodcut, 298 x 210 mm.
B. 92

Meder 204, before the text edition, a
Watermark: High crown (M. 20)
Maria Antoinette Evans Fund   M32083

This is one of the most coherent and expressive compositions among the seventeen early woodcuts of the *Life of the Virgin*. The post of the gateway functions very economically to emphasize the separation of Christ and his Mother. The figure of Mary seated on the ground and supported by another woman suggests the sorrowing Virgin at the foot of the cross. The gatepost itself, with its great brace, may have been intended as a reminder of the cross on which Christ was to die.

The superb quality of this strong, clear, well-preserved impression intensifies the expressiveness of the image.

80. Christ among the Doctors (reduced)

81. Christ Taking Leave from His Mother (reduced)

82. Glorification of the Virgin (reduced)

82

Glorification of the Virgin

Probably 1500–1501
From the *Life of the Virgin*
Woodcut, 296 x 213 mm.
B. 95

Meder 207, before the text edition, a
Watermark: High crown (M. 20)
Maria Antoinette Evans Fund   M32089

The *Glorification of the Virgin* is believed to be the first
woodcut in the *Life of the Virgin* that Dürer executed. The
crowding of the figures and the diffusion of interest owing
to such anecdotal details as the playful putti in the foreground testify to the earliness of the composition. Panofsky
suggests that this print, like the *Sojourn in Egypt* (cat. no.
79), was originally conceived as a devotional image.
Because of the prominence of the curtained bed in the
background, the two blank heraldic shields held by the
putti, and various other symbols, he thinks that the print
was intended to be given to a bride and groom at the time
of their marriage.

In the 1511 text edition, the print was used to close the
series. The colophon below the image reads, in translation:
"Printed at Nuremberg by Albrecht Dürer, painter, the
year of our Lord 1511" and is followed by a warning to
copyists.

The impression is very strong and carefully printed so
that the multitude of detail reads with maximum clarity.

For the remaining subjects in the *Life of the Virgin*, see
cat. nos. 161–165.

83

Saint George on Horseback

About 1504
Woodcut, 212 x 143 mm.
B. 111

Meder 225b
No visible watermark
Coll.: Tomás Harris
Stephen Bullard Memorial Fund   68.245

In the diary Dürer kept in the Netherlands, his entry of
November 24, 1520, in Antwerp, mentions selling seven of
his *Schlectes Holzwerk*. This term has been interpreted in
two ways: according to modern usage, the phrase would
mean "bad work on wood"; according to a secondary
meaning (for which the German word *schlict* is now
commonly used), it would mean "simple or homely woodcuts." The latter translation could imply that the woodcuts
were less elaborate than those Dürer was accustomed to
designing and were intended to be sold as popular images
to the general public. Both interpretations are, in a sense,
correct. The term has been applied to *Saint George on Horseback* and ten other woodcuts of similar format with Dürer's
monogram that have been ascribed to the years 1504–1505.
Panofsky suggests that the whole group, composed of
saints, two Holy Families, and a Crucifixion, was intended
for a devotional book of saints. If this is true, Dürer may
have simply left his drawings with the publisher for trans-
fer to the blocks. In 1504, he was preoccupied with the
Life of the Virgin, and the following year he set out for Italy.
The group of eleven seem to have been cut by at least two
rather unskilled woodblock cutters. In any case, they were
certainly not cut by the same master craftsmen who,
probably under Dürer's close supervision, cut the *Life of
the Virgin.* None of the eleven "schlectes" woodcuts is
particularly rare. The fact that Dürer carried them to the
Netherlands would indicate that he was not totally ashamed
of them.

This fine, early impression of *Saint George on Horseback*
conveys the sophistication of Dürer's original design of
horse and rider locked in combat with the dragon. Although
the print is effective as a two-dimensional pattern, the
crudeness of cutting precluded any suggestion of depth.
The contour lines are thick and lack variety, and it appears
the cutter was not able to reproduce Dürer's delicate cross-
hatchings in the area surrounding the horse. The face of
the maiden in the background is incompletely defined.

83. Saint George on Horseback

84–85

The Fall of Man (Adam and Eve)
Dated 1504
Engraving, 252 x 195 mm.
B. 1

84

Meder 1, II, a
Watermark: Bull's head (M. 62)
Colls.: Friedrich August II (Lugt 971), Tomás Harris
Centennial Gift of Landon T. Clay   68.187

Here seen in a magnificent impression, the figures of Adam and Eve are the culmination of Dürer's intensive investigation of the proportions of the ideal man and woman. The importance of the plate to Dürer is indicated by the unusually large number of surviving drawings that relate to the composition. And, on this one print, the artist signed his name in full: "Albrecht Dürer of Nuremberg made [this], 1504."

There exist rare trial proofs from the unfinished plate that illuminate the artist's method of working. These proofs reveal that Dürer's vision of the final image was so clearly fixed that he was able to complete whole sections of the plate in every detail while other sections of the plate were still in the outline stage.

The woodland setting, slightly reminiscent of the *Saint Eustace* (cat. no. 59), serves as a backdrop for the figures of Adam and Eve, who stand before it like antique statues. Just as the human figure is constructed according to a canon of proportion, so is nature brought under intellectual control, idealized, and made regular.

A new element that enters Dürer's engravings with this print is a sense of light playing on the forms. This active, sparkling light rapidly disappears as the plate wears. Compare in the following impression the transparent shadow cast by one of Adam's legs on the other (see details) and that cast by the fig branch on Eve's thigh.

The animals represented are more than the livestock of Paradise; they have a symbolic import related to the Fall of Man (see Panofsky, vol. I, pp. 84–85).

85

Meder 1, III, a
Watermark: Bull's head (M. 62)
Colls.: A. Bourduge (Lugt 70), H. F. Sewall (Lugt 1309)
Harvey D. Parker Collection   P247

This later state of the engraving is identified by the addition of a cleft in the tree under Adam's left arm, a change presumably made by Dürer.

According to Meder, the Bull's Head watermark, which is found in both impressions exhibited, is not necessarily an indication of an early printing for it may be found up to about 1519.

The plate has worn and no longer prints as strongly. Beside the loss of the special effects of light, there is a diminution in modeling: Adam's flesh appears to have fewer muscles; Eve's, fewer soft curves. Specific textures become more general: the metallic crispness of Adam's hair has softened.

The paper is somewhat discolored, which further lessens contrasts. There are numerous small repairs to the sheet, which has been clipped at the right and has had the upper right corner replaced.

84. The Fall of Man

85. The Fall of Man

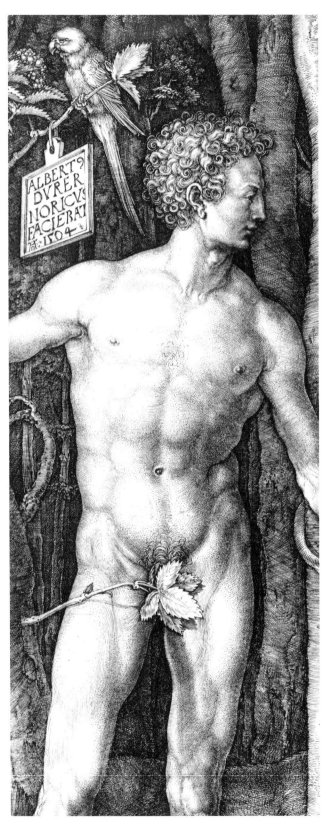

84a. The Fall of Man (enlarged detail)

85a. The Fall of Man (enlarged detail)

86–89

The Nativity
Dated 1504
Engraving, 182 x 122 mm.
B. 2

86

Meder 2b-c
Watermark: Bull's head (M. 62)
Coll.: E. Th. Rodenacker (Lugt 2438)
Katherine Eliot Bullard Fund   1971.218

Referred to by Dürer in the diary of his Netherlands
journey as *Weihnachten* or "Christmas," this virtuoso
engraving displays, in smaller format, the same profusion
of textures as the *Saint Eustace* (cat. no. 59) but now ordered
by a rational perspective framework. In spite of its lucid
structure, this is an image that one must pore over in order
to read each lovingly described detail, each nuance of color
and texture. In this fine early impression, an excess of ink
is visible in areas such as the thatched roof, giving an
added suggestion of color to the image. The smudge of ink
between the boards above the arch opening on the landscape is not the result of this excess of ink but is produced
by an accidentally roughened area in the plate that prints
only in fine early impressions.

87

Meder 2c-d
Watermark: Bull's head (M. 62)
Coll.: H. F. Sewall (Lugt 1309)
Harvey D. Parker Collection   P248

The plate has worn; every trace of burr has disappeared;
the subtle differentiation of surface texture so characteristic
of early impressions of this print has totally vanished; and
the original strong illusion of perspective is negated.

   Discoloration of the paper has contracted the space;
note, for example, the diminished effect of the landscape
with the descending angel. This darkening of the paper
has also removed all suggestion of light and atmosphere.
The upper left corner of the sheet moved in the press
during the printing, producing a blurred effect.

88

Meder 2c-f
No visible watermark
Coll.: Tomás Harris
Frederick Keppel Memorial Bequest, by sale of duplicates
68.270

The plate has been reduced to a mere skeleton of contour
lines. There is only one texture, one color in the impression. The image is further flattened by the printing of an
even gray tone of ink over its whole surface.

89

JAN WIERIX
Flemish, circa 1549–after 1615
Copy after Dürer, B. 2
Engraving, Alvin* 152, I, 182 x 118 mm.
Coll.: H. F. Sewall (Lugt 1309)
Harvey D. Parker Collection   P6794

The inscription engraved on the block of stone at the far
right (I·H·W·Æ 16·1566) informs us that the artist was
Jan Wierix, age sixteen. Although a remarkable accomp-
lishment for this precocious member of a Flemish family of
professional engravers, this copy can only lead us to better
appreciate the qualities of Dürer's original. In place of
Dürer's spectrum of fine textures and subtle suggestions of
color, we are presented with an overall hard, glossy texture
(see details). There is a greater emphasis on the edges of
forms than on the description of their surfaces.

   As seen here, fully signed and dated, the print was not
intended to deceive, but later impressions are recorded in
which the Wierix monogram and the date have been removed from the plate and replaced by stippling. The
Museum also owns an impression in which the identifying
monogram and date have been scraped from the paper.
Impressions without Wierix' monogram have been brought
for examination to the Department of Prints and Drawings
by collectors who believed them to be from Dürer's original
plate.

*Louis Alvin, *Catalogue raisonné de l'oeuvre des Trois frères Jean,
Jérome et Antoine Wierix* (Brussels, 1866).

86. The Nativity

87. The Nativity

88. The Nativity

89. The Nativity (copy)

86a. The Nativity (enlarged detail)

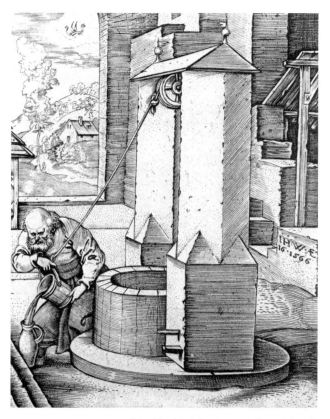

89a. The Nativity (copy, enlarged detail)

90

The Small Horse
Dated 1505
Engraving, 163 x 108 mm.
B. 96

Meder 93a
No visible watermark
Coll.: G. W. Wales (Lugt 2544)
Wales Collection   M1743

Like the *Fall of Man* (cat. no. 84) of the preceding year, this plate grew out of Dürer's studies of the canons of proportion for man and beast. The profile view permits accurate measurement and comparison of the parts to the whole. The horse in the woodcut *Saint George* of about 1504 (cat. no. 83) was treated similarly.

This is a very rich, black, and early impression in rather dubious condition. A small hole in the arch at the upper left has been mended. Several large patches have been applied to the back of the sheet, which was then mounted down on another piece of paper and a heavy border added with pen and black ink.

Panofsky has suggested that the butterfly-winged helmet and winged boots of the groom signify Perseus or Mercury.

90. The Small Horse

91. The Large Horse

91
The Large Horse
Dated 1505
Engraving, 166 x 119 mm.
B. 97

Meder 94a
Watermark: Bull's head (M. 62)
Colls.: J. Maberly, H. F. Sewall, 1850 (Lugt 1309)
Harvey D. Parker Collection   P363

The oblique angle makes it unlikely that this horse was a
study of ideal proportions, as was the *Small Horse* (cat. no.
90) or the *Fall of Man* (cat. no. 84). It is, rather, a representation of the essential natural qualities of an individual
horse. In further contrast to the *Small Horse,* the attendant's
antique armor is elaborate but more earthly.

This impression is strong, early, and in fine condition
with very wide margins. The printed lines stand up in
their original high relief on an unabraded surface.

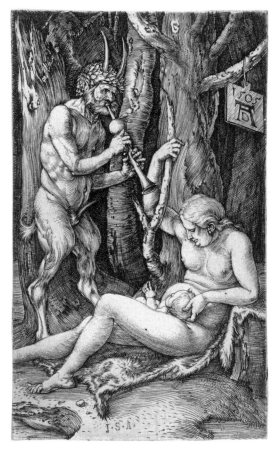

92. Musical Satyr and Nymph with Baby

92
Musical Satyr and Nymph with Baby
(Satyr's Family)
Dated 1505
Engraving, 116 x 71 mm.
B. 69

Meder 65b
Watermark: Bull's head (M. 62)
Colls.: J. St. Aubyn (Lugt 1534), H. F. Sewall (Lugt 1309)
Harvey D. Parker Collection   P333

Dürer shared with other Renaissance artists and scholars
not only an interest in ideal proportion but also an interest
in pagan mythology. Mythological subjects are numerous
among the engravings of Jacopo de' Barbari (a Venetian
painter who worked in Nuremberg from 1500 to 1503 and
remained in Germany and the Netherlands until about
1516). Dürer's own writings state how disappointed he
was that de' Barbari would not teach him what he (de'
Barbari) had learned of ideal proportions. There are
obvious similarities between various engravings by the
two artists, but since de' Barbari never dated his prints,
it is impossible to know whether Dürer's engravings
influenced de' Barbari or the reverse.

In the *Satyr's Family*, the similarity is not only one of
subject matter but also one of treatment. The long, curving
parallel strokes are typical of the Venetian artist's engravings. Moreover, the physical type of the female figure is
clearly related to engravings by de' Barbari, such as his
Venus (see Hind, vol. V, p. 154, no. 18).

This is a strong impression in good condition. It lacks
only the extra depth of shadow in the woods that burr
produces in the earliest impressions.

93–108
ENGRAVED PASSION
1507–1512

Of the fifteen plates comprising this series, five were engraved between 1507 and 1511 and the remaining ten in 1512. The most likely reason for Dürer's delay in completing the *Engraved Passion* is that he was engaged in the preparation of the three large woodcut books (*Apocalypse, Large Passion,* and *Life of the Virgin*) and the woodcut *Small Passion,* published in 1511.

Unlike the woodcut books, the Passion engravings were not accompanied by a text, but from Dürer's Netherlands diary, we know that he customarily sold them as a set. Early purchasers often bound them as a book and sometimes had the engravings colored, with highlights added in gold and silver.

Dürer's engravings are more sombre and restrained in their presentation of Christ's Passion than either the large or small woodcut versions. The fineness of the engraved lines enabled Dürer to suggest in these scenes an almost spiritual light. The same fineness also made possible a greater exploration of facial expression, thereby expanding psychological dimensions.

The *Engraved Passion* scenes have a compelling forthrightness and grandeur owing to the prominence of the participants who occupy most of the available space. The consistent placement of the figures in the foreground unifies the series.

With the exception of the earliest print, the 1507 *Lamentation* (cat. no. 105), Dürer has defined the limits of the shallow space by two devices: either parallel shading lines that depict darkness or dark-toned architectural backgrounds. (In the *Deposition of Christ,* cat. no. 106, the rocks behind the figures perform the same function as the architecture.) Both shading and architecture often serve as an intermediate tone between the darkest shadows and the highlights created by the blank paper. This increased tonal range and the shallow space combine to produce an effect of high relief sculpture.

The impressions exhibited here are consistently good and well printed. However, no single one manifests the brilliance, richness, and effect of gleaming metal that is characteristic of the earliest impressions. All of the prints have been cut to the plate mark. They were also glued down at one time and have suffered damages when removed, particularly at the four corners.

93
Man of Sorrows by the Column
Dated 1509
From the *Engraved Passion*
117 x 74 mm.
B. 3

Meder 3b–c
Watermark: High crown (M. 20)
Gift of Edward Habich   M8835

The Man of Sorrows by the Column is a devotional image rather than part of the narrative of the Passion. Christ, with the wounds of the Crucifixion, stands holding the instruments of the Flagellation beside the column to which he was bound.

93. Man of Sorrows by the Column

94
Agony in the Garden
Dated 1508
From the *Engraved Passion*
117 x 74 mm.
B. 4

Meder 4c
No visible watermark
Gift of Edward Habich   M8836

The *Agony in the Garden* of 1508 is one of the first engravings in which Dürer darkened the whole sky with horizontal shading. This is also to be seen in the *Betrayal of Christ* of the same year (cat. no. 95) and the *Crucifixion* of 1511 (cat. no. 104). Here the shading of the sky successfully describes the nocturnal setting and heightens the effect of the light that radiates from the angel.

Black flecks, most clearly visible on the left knee of Peter asleep in the foreground, were probably produced by imperfections in the metal plate which retained ink.

94. Agony in the Garden

95. Betrayal of Christ

95
Betrayal of Christ
Dated 1508
From the *Engraved Passion*
117 x 74 mm.
B. 5

Meder 5c
Watermark: High crown (M. 20)
Gift of Edward Habich   M8837

Here, as in the *Agony in the Garden,* the horizontal shading of the sky denotes darkness. It also establishes an intermediate tone between the brightest highlights and the deepest shadows. The increased tonal range enables Dürer to give added volume to his figures so that the highlights have a great dramatic impact.

96

Christ before Caiaphas
Dated 1512
From the *Engraved Passion*
117 x 74 mm.
B. 6

Meder 6a
No visible watermark
Gift of Edward Habich   M8838

Most of the ten subjects dated 1512 are crowded with
participants — high priests, soldiers, and onlookers —
posturing in exotic costumes. A stage-like feeling is
created by the shallow space of the architecture, the placement of the principal figures in the foreground, and the
liberal use of steps and platforms for dramatic emphasis.

97. Christ before Pilate for the First Time

96. Christ before Caiaphas

97

Christ before Pilate for the First Time
Dated 1512
From the *Engraved Passion*
117 x 74 mm.
B. 7

Meder 7c
No visible watermark
Gift of Edward Habich   M8839

As may be seen by this example, the ten 1512 plates of the
Engraved Passion are heavily worked with hatching,
cross-hatching, flicks, and stippling in a great variety of
combinations to depict shading and texture.

98
Flagellation of Christ
Dated 1512
From the *Engraved Passion*
117 x 74 mm.
B. 8

Meder 8c
No visible watermark
Gift of Edward Habich   M8840

99
Christ Crowned with Thorns
Dated 1512
From the *Engraved Passion*
117 x 74 mm.
B. 9

Meder 9b
No visible watermark
Gift of Edward Habich   M8841

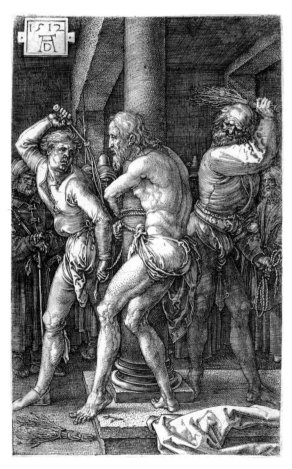

98. Flagellation of Christ

99. Christ Crowned with Thorns

100. *Ecce Homo*

101. Pilate Washing His Hands

100

Ecce Homo (Christ Presented to the People)
Dated 1512
From the *Engraved Passion*
117 x 74 mm.
B. 10

Meder 10b
No visible watermark
Gift of Edward Habich   M8842

In this exhibition, the *Ecce Homo* is the first engraving to
show an expressive use of tonal inking. A film of ink left
on the plate appears in the impression on the platform with
Dürer's monogram and on the legs of Christ. This tone
heightens the effect of brilliant white areas where the
excess ink had been wiped away, such as Christ's tense
shoulders and bound hands or the cloak of the exotically
garbed man at the right.

101

Pilate Washing His Hands
Dated 1512
From the *Engraved Passion*
117 x 74 mm.
B. 11

Meder 11a
No visible watermark
Gift of Edward Habich   M8843

Slight soiling of the paper diminishes the bright atmospheric effect of the sky at upper right.

102. Bearing of the Cross

103. Bearing of the Cross

102–103

Bearing of the Cross
Dated 1512
From the *Engraved Passion*
117 x 74 mm.
B. 12

102
Meder 12b
No visible watermark
Gift of Edward Habich   M8844

103
Meder 12b-c
No visible watermark
Gift of Mrs. Samuel Cabot   51.2403

This impression, in which the tablet in the upper right corner lacks its tab, was considered at the time of its acquisition in 1951 to be an earlier state of the plate (*MFA Bulletin* 50 (1952), 10f; and noted in Hollstein, vol. VII, p. 12). However, a recent examination of the upper right corner with the assistance of a microscope revealed a patch and skillful pen work. The apparent difference in state was the result of restoration of the sheet rather than of changes made in the plate.

104. Crucifixion

105

Lamentation
Dated 1507
From the *Engraved Passion*
117 x 71 mm.
B. 14

Meder 14a–b
No visible watermark
Gift of Edward Habich   M8846

The *Lamentation* is the earliest of the *Engraved Passion* subjects, and it is somewhat lighter in tonality than most of the prints in the series.

104

Crucifixion
Dated 1511
From the *Engraved Passion*
117 x 74 mm.
B. 13

Meder 13d
Watermark: Bull's head (M. 64)
Gift of Edward Habich   M8845

This impression of the *Crucifixion* is rather unevenly inked and printed. Along the lower left edge many lines did not fully print, and an attempt was made to rectify this by drawing in the borderline and the first number of the date.

105. Lamentation

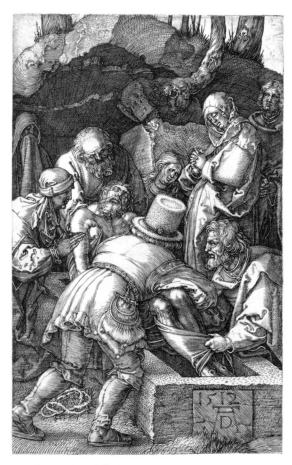

106. Deposition of Christ

107. Harrowing of Hell

106

Deposition of Christ (Entombment)
Dated 1512
From the *Engraved Passion*
117 x 74 mm.
B. 15

Meder 15c(?)
No visible watermark
Gift of Edward Habich   M8847

A light film of ink left on the plate darkens the sky and the
overhanging rock. This tonal inking is, however, less
expressive than that in the *Ecce Homo* (cat. no. 100) and
may have been accidental.

107

Harrowing of Hell
Dated 1512
From the *Engraved Passion*
115 x 74 mm.
B. 16

Meder 16c
No visible watermark
Gift of Edward Habich   M8848

108. Resurrection

108
Resurrection
Dated 1512
From the *Engraved Passion*
117 x 74 mm.
B. 17

Meder 17c
No visible watermark
Gift of Edward Habich   M8849

A glue stain, resulting from the mounting of the print, has made a yellowish spot in the aureole above Christ's head.

109
The Madonna with the Pear
Dated 1511
Engraving, 157 x 107 mm.
B. 41

Meder 33a
No visible watermark
Coll.: Tomás Harris
Katherine Eliot Bullard Fund   68.204

The Madonna with the Pear is, with regard to structuring of light and shadow, closely related to three plates in the *Engraved Passion*: the *Agony* and *Betrayal* of 1508 and the *Crucifixion* of 1511 (cat. nos. 94, 95, 104). The figures are conceived as broad masses of light and dark set against a shaded background. The combination of the darkened sky and the strong theatrical illumination that picks out the Virgin and Child creates great uncertainty about whether day or night was intended. In areas of shadow, forms merge and flow together in a painterly manner. Dürer's customary strong interest in variety of texture and detail in his engravings has been tempered in favor of breadth and consistency. Shading and tonal color are achieved primarily by parallel lines engraved close together. These lines often curve round the forms they model, thereby intensifying the impression of volume and here give a feeling of amplitude, of abundance to the figures of the Virgin and Child. This vocabulary of parallel lines may be found not only in the *Engraved Passion* but also in the *Large Passion* woodcuts of 1510 and the single-sheet woodcuts of 1511. During these years, woodcut was Dürer's favored means of expression in printmaking. There are no engravings dated 1510, and the only other engraving dated 1511 is the *Crucifixion* from the *Engraved Passion* (cat. no. 104).

136

109. The Madonna with the Pear

110–111
TWO PATTERNS FOR EMBROIDERY ("KNOTS")
1506–1507
B. 141 and 143

110
Second Knot with an Oblong Tablet
Woodcut, 269 x 207 mm.
Meder 275, I, a–b
No visible watermark
Stephen Bullard Memorial Fund   38.1744b

111
**Fourth Knot with Seven Circular Groups of Knots
with Black Centers**
Woodcut, 271 x 212 mm.
Meder 277, I
Watermark: Cardinal's hat (M. 44)
Stephen Bullard Memorial Fund   38.1744d

The set of six ornamental woodcuts called "Knots" by
Dürer in his Netherlands diary may have been designs to
be carried out in embroidery or lace. They do not consist
of one intertwined thread, but of several patterns repeated
and interlaced. The woodcuts are, in fact, modified copies
of engravings that are inscribed: *Academia Leonardi Vinci*
(see Hind, vol. V, pp. 93–95, nos. 19–24). Although there
was no formal academy or art school conducted by
Leonardo, the designs are characteristic of his ornamental
style. It is probable that Dürer became acquainted with
them during his second visit to Venice from 1505 to 1507.
In comparison with the Leonardesque engraving, Dürer's
woodcuts are bolder, more calligraphic, and more two-
dimensional in effect.

It is unusual to find Dürer in the role of copyist, and the
exact date and place of the execution of the blocks is also
a puzzle. The earliest states, as in these two examples from
the Museum's set, are printed on a fine quality Italian
paper. The Cardinal's hat watermark seen on most impressions of the first state is also found on a drawing dated
1506 for Dürer's painting *The Feast of the Rose Garlands,*
painted in Venice. Posthumous states of four of the
"knots" with Dürer's monogram added in the center
medallions are to be found printed on paper with a
German watermark of the last half of the sixteenth century.

The uneven quality of the black areas does not imply
carelessness in printing, but is characteristic of the way a
broad, flat surface of wood prints on paper.

110. Second Knot with an Oblong Tablet (reduced)

139

111. Fourth Knot with Seven Circular Groups of Knots with Black Centers (reduced)

140

112–152
SMALL PASSION
1509–1511

Unlike the *Large Passion* (cat. nos. 47–57, 154–160) and the *Engraved Passion* (cat. nos. 93–108), the *Small Passion* in woodcut was conceived as a whole, executed within a brief span of time. It was published as a book in 1511, the year in which Dürer's "Three Large Books" appeared. Four of the woodcuts are dated, two 1509 and two 1510 (see cat. nos. 131, 136, 114, 137, respectively). Chelidonius, the poet associated with the *Large Passion* and the *Life of the Virgin*, wrote Latin verses that were paired with a facing woodcut in the book.

The *Small Passion* is extraordinarily comprehensive, consisting of a title page and thirty-six woodcuts, instead of the more usual eleven or fourteen subjects Dürer used in his other two *Passions*. He put the events of the Passion into historical perspective by beginning with man's fall and his expulsion from Eden. He followed these subjects with the Annunciation and the birth of Christ, who was to redeem man from the original sin that caused his fall. Dürer then turned to the Passion proper, through which men were given the possibility of salvation. The work ends with the Last Judgment where some of the dead can be seen entering the jaws of hell and others turning towards heaven.

The book must have had a popular appeal because of its stress on the human, sometimes prosaic, aspects of the Passion narrative. Dürer retold the story as an eyewitness might, with vividness and attention to minute detail. He recorded the events and their effect not only on Christ but also on his followers, his persecutors, and on the four officials who examined him five times. As the woodcuts are modest in scale, so are they simple and straight-forward in content.

Because of the relatively short time involved in the execution, printing, and publication of the *Small Passion* blocks, it is difficult to establish a precise sequence of printings. A few impressions have been recorded of earlier states, before certain changes were made on the blocks (as, for example, cat. no. 134). There are a large number of early impressions from the completed blocks without text on the versos. Some of these impressions without text display some of the borderline breaks and other damages which Meder ascribes to impressions from the 1511 book edition. It is very unlikely that all the sets with text were printed in 1511. More probably, additional sets were printed according to demand during the following years.

Impressions without text also exist that appear to have been printed at about the same time as the 1511 edition with text. For most of the blocks, Meder describes three further printings without text up to about 1550, distinguishing them by watermarks and by the condition of the blocks.

In 1612, the blocks were printed in Venice by Daniel Bissuccio (see cat. no. 126). Meder records further late impressions from the blocks showing extensive damage and many wormholes.

Shortly after thirty-five of the blocks were acquired by the British Museum, London, in 1839, stereotypes were made from them in which the borderline breaks and wormholes were filled. Meder lists six nineteenth-century printings from the stereotype plates. John Thompson (1785–1866), a wood engraver, examined the woodblocks in the British Museum and suggested that at least four different hands took part in the cutting; he cited cat. nos. 132, 138, 145, and 146 as having enough individual differences in cutting technique to lead to that conclusion.

In the *Small Passion*, Dürer for the first time introduced into his woodcuts, as he already had in two 1508 *Engraved Passion*, plates (*Agony*, cat. no. 94, and *Betrayal*, cat. no. 95), middle gray tones through the use of parallel hatchings and cross-hatchings. The regularity of the lines in the new style made them easier for the cutter to execute; the fewer variations he had to contend with, the easier his task.

Most of the impressions exhibited here are from the Henry F. Sewall Collection, which was purchased by the Museum with money from the Harvey D. Parker Fund in 1897. The majority are early impressions, fine in quality, and in good condition.

Paffio Chzifti ab Alberto Durer Nu
renbergenfi effigiata cū varij generis carmi
nibus Fratris Benedicti Chelidonij
Mufophili.

O mihi tantorum, iufto mihi caufa dolorum
O crucis O mortis caufa cruenta mihi.
O homo fat fuerit, tibi me femel ifta tuliffe.
O ceffa culpis me cruciare nouis.

Cum priuilegio.

112. Man of Sorrows Seated, title page

112
Man of Sorrows Seated

1509–1511
Title page from the *Small Passion*
Woodcut, 85 x 81 mm.
B. 16

Meder 125, 1511 edition with Latin text
No visible watermark
Colls.: A. Morrison, H. Oppenheimer, Tomás Harris
Centennial Gift of Landon T. Clay   68.193

Meder describes a unique proof in the British Museum,
London, in which the title was cut in Gothic letters. There
was a grammatical error in the Latin title, and for the
1511 edition, the letters were discarded and a new title
set in Roman type. The block for the *Man of Sorrows* must
have been lost or destroyed soon after the 1511 edition
for it was never printed again.

113
The Fall of Man

1510–1511
From the *Small Passion*
Woodcut, 126 x 97 mm.
B. 17

Meder 126, after 1511, without text, a–b
No visible watermark
Coll.: W. G. Russell Allen
Gift of Mrs. C. Tunnard in memory of W. G. Russell Allen
61.1354

On the basis of Meder's description of the wearing of the
block and quality of impression, this may be dated after
the text edition of 1511 and probably before 1550. Nevertheless, it is still quite strong and clear.

113. The Fall of Man

114. Expulsion from Paradise

print as nearly solid areas. For this reason, the woods in the background lack depth and variety.

There are rare early impressions in which Eve's spine has more shading. It is probable that Dürer removed the hatchings deliberately, thus creating a new state.

The paper has yellowed considerably, and there are many tears and repairs.

115
Annunciation
1509–1511
From the *Small Passion*
Woodcut, 128 x 97 mm.
B. 19

Meder 128, before the text edition
No visible watermark
Colls.: J. Barnard, F. Garford, H. F. Sewall
Harvey D. Parker Collection   P18

This impression has some, though not all, of the breaks in the borderline Meder ascribes to the 1511 text edition. The fine lines have a clarity that is lacking in the two preceding impressions printed after the 1511 edition. Because of the fineness and delicacy of the lines and the light inking of the block, the impression has a silvery tonality.

The impression is slightly uneven. The discoloration in the corners was perhaps caused by glue used to mount the prints. This discoloration is also visible on many of the other prints in the Parker set.

114
Expulsion from Paradise
Dated 1510
From the *Small Passion*
Woodcut, 126 x 97 mm.
B. 18

Meder 127, after 1511, without text, c
Watermark: Bear (M. 86)
Colls.: J. Barnard, F. Garford, H. F. Sewall
Harvey D. Parker Collection   P17

This impression of the *Expulsion* is somewhat later than that of the *Fall of Man,* and its rather thick lines testify to many printings of the block. The block was also over-inked, and the lines in the densest areas of cross-hatching

116
Nativity
1509–1511
From the *Small Passion*
Woodcut, 128 x 102 mm.
B. 20

Meder 129, before the text edition
No visible watermark
Colls.: J. Barnard, F. Garford, H. F. Sewall
Harvey D. Parker Collection   P19

116. Nativity

115. Annunciation

117. Entry into Jerusalem

118. Christ Driving the Money Lenders from the Temple

117

Entry into Jerusalem

1509–1511
From the *Small Passion*
Woodcut, 128 x 97 mm.
B. 22

Meder 130, before the text edition
No visible watermark
Colls.: J. Barnard, F. Garford, H. F. Sewall
Harvey D. Parker Collection   P21

This impression has been printed from a heavily inked
block, as can be seen by the extra ink between the lines of
Christ's aureole. The block has three of the breaks in the
top borderline which Meder associates with the 1511
text edition.

118

Christ Driving the Money Lenders from the Temple

1509–1511
From the *Small Passion*
Woodcut, 126 x 97 mm.
B. 23

Meder 131, before the text edition
No visible watermark
Colls.: J. Barnard, F. Garford, H. F. Sewall
Harvey D. Parker Collection   P22

The unevenness of this print can be attributed to unskill-
ful cutting of the block, rather than to careless inking or
printing, since the same effect is to be seen in all early
impressions.

119. Christ Taking Leave from His Mother

119

Christ Taking Leave from His Mother

1509–1511
From the *Small Passion*
Woodcut, 126 x 97 mm.
B. 21

Meder 132, before the text edition
No visible watermark
Colls.: J. Barnard, F. Garford, H. F. Sewall
Harvey D. Parker Collection   P20

This impression is a strong and satisfactory one. A break
in the borderline, top right, has been filled in with brush.

120

Last Supper

1509–1511

From the *Small Passion*

Woodcut, 126 x 99 mm.

B. 24

Meder 133, before the text edition
Watermark: Bull's head (M. 70)
Colls.: J. Barnard, F. Garford, H. F. Sewall
Harvey D. Parker Collection   P23

121

Christ Washing the Feet of the Disciples

1509–1511

From the *Small Passion*

Woodcut, 126 x 99 mm.

B. 25

Meder 134, before the text edition
Watermark: Bull's head (M. 70)
Colls.: J. Barnard, F. Garford, H. F. Sewall
Harvey D. Parker Collection   P24

122

Agony in the Garden

1509–1511

From the *Small Passion*

Woodcut, 126 x 97 mm.

B. 26

Meder 135, before the text edition
No visible watermark
Colls.: J. Barnard, F. Garford, H. F. Sewall
Harvey D. Parker Collection   P25

120. Last Supper

122. Agony in the Garden

121. Christ Washing the Feet of the Disciples

123
Betrayal of Christ
1509–1511
From the *Small Passion*
Woodcut, 126 x 97 mm.
B. 27

Meder 136, before the text edition
Watermark: Bull's head (M. 70)
Colls.: J. Barnard, F. Garford, H. F. Sewall
Harvey D. Parker Collection   P26

This impression is both strong and well printed.

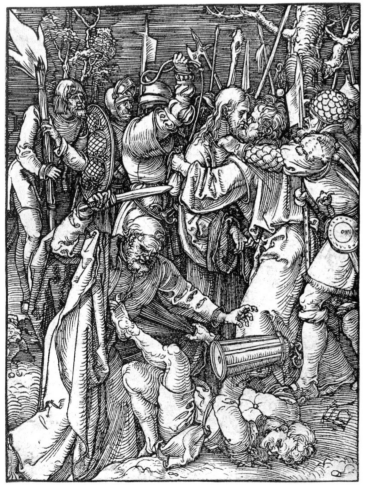

123. Betrayal of Christ

124–127
Christ before Annas
1509–1511
From the *Small Passion*
Woodcut, 127 x 97 mm.
B. 28

124
Meder 137, before the text edition
No visible watermark
Colls.: J. Barnard, F. Garford, H. F. Sewall
Harvey D. Parker Collection   P27

This impression is a good one, but it is not as early as most of the other impressions before the 1511 text edition in this exhibition. Meder describes the earliest impressions, and the earliest of those in the 1511 edition with text, as having complete borderlines, while other impressions, printed toward the end of the 1511 edition, have a number of breaks in the borderline. In this impression, some, but not all, of the breaks have occurred, for example, those just under Dürer's monogram visible in the impression from the 1511 edition (cat. no. 125).

On the basis of this evidence alone, it can be stated that during the time that the edition with text was being printed, additional impressions without it were issued.

125
Meder 137, 1511 edition with Latin text
No visible watermark
Coll.: H. F. Sewall (Lugt 1309)
Harvey D. Parker Collection   P18651

This impression, with text on the verso, has all of the breaks in the lower borderline Meder describes for the 1511 edition. A rather large one below the legs of Christ has been drawn in with ink. The impression is still relatively good, though the lines in the woodblock had begun to thicken, and the printing ink appears to have been heavier than in the earlier impression. Both factors affect the clarity of the printed lines, as may be seen, for example, in the cross-hatching of the soldiers' clothes.

More disturbing than the heaviness of inking is a repair in the face of the soldier beating Christ. A large tear was patched and his features clumsily redrawn.

125. Christ before Annas

124. Christ before Annas

126. Christ before Annas

127. Christ before Annas (cop[y]

126

Meder 137, 1612 edition with Italian text
No visible watermark
Coll.: H. F. Sewall (Lugt 1309)
Harvey D. Parker Collection   P18652

In 1612, Daniel Bissuccio published the *Small Passion* blocks in Venice with Italian verses by Mauritio Moro. As one would expect, the blocks by then were considerably worn and damaged. In this example, a large crack cuts through the horizontal hatching in the upper left corner. Lines that define outer contours of figures have widened to such an extent that the proper balance between these lines and the fine, interior modeling lines is destroyed. The result is an overall flattening of volumes.

127

Meder 137, Mommard copy
127 x 101 mm.
No visible watermark
Gift of Thomas Gaffield   M11100

In 1587, Johann Mommard of Brussels published copies of the *Small Passion* woodcuts with a new title page. The copies were reissued in 1644. The Mommard copies are deceptive because a line for line comparison with good impressions of the originals could lead one to believe they are late, poor impressions. Still, it is possible to distinguish the copies because, as careful as they are, there are discrepancies in the lines. Meder gives clear descriptions and also reproduces some of the obvious differences between the copies and the originals. In this copy, the monogram differs from the original. Furthermore, on the left leg of the soldier pulling Christ's hair, the copyist failed to understand both the folds of the stocking at the ankle and the buckle of the shoes.

A more decisive factor than a line for line comparison in distinguishing the copy from the original is the overall effect of Mommard's copy. The subtle differences in tone and volume created by Dürer's variations of the width of his lines and the spaces between them are not present in the copy. As a result, there is a confusion of planes and the architectural setting seems shallower.

128

Christ before Caiaphas

1509–1511
From the *Small Passion*
Woodcut, 124 x 99 mm.
B. 29

Meder 138, before the text edition
No visible watermark
Colls.: J. Barnard, F. Garford, H. F. Sewall
Harvey D. Parker Collection   P28

128. Christ before Caiaphas

129. Mocking of Christ

129

Mocking of Christ

1509–1511
From the *Small Passion*
Woodcut, 126 x 97 mm.
B. 30

Meder 139, before the text edition
Watermark: Bull's head (M. 70)
Colls.: J. Barnard, F. Garford, H. F. Sewall
Harvey D. Parker Collection   P29

130

Christ before Pilate for the First Time

1509–1511
From the *Small Passion*
Woodcut, 126 x 97 mm.
B. 31

Meder 140, before the text edition
No visible watermark
Colls.: J. Barnard, F. Garford, H. F. Sewall
Harvey D. Parker Collection   P30

This is a fine impression of one of Dürer's most interestingly composed woodcuts in the *Small Passion*. The placement of the figures lends stability to an irrational architectural setting.

131

Christ before Herod

Dated 1509
From the *Small Passion*
Woodcut, 126 x 97 mm.
B. 32

Meder 141, before the text edition
No visible watermark
Colls.: J. Barnard, F. Garford, H. F. Sewall
Harvey D. Parker Collection   P31

131. Christ before Herod

130. Christ before Pilate for the First Time

132

Flagellation of Christ
1509–1511
From the *Small Passion*
Woodcut, 126 x 97 mm.
B. 33

Meder 142, before the text edition
Watermark: Bull's head (M. 70)
Colls.: J. Barnard, F. Garford, H. F. Sewall
Harvey D. Parker Collection   P32

133

Christ Crowned with Thorns
1509–1511
From the *Small Passion*
Woodcut, 124 x 97 mm.
B. 34

Meder 143, before the text edition
No visible watermark
Colls.: J. Barnard, F. Garford, H. F. Sewall
Harvey D. Parker Collection   P33

134

Ecce Homo (Christ Presented to the People)
1509–1511
From the *Small Passion*
Woodcut, 127 x 97 mm.
B. 35

Meder 144, first state, before the text edition
Watermark: Bull's head (M. 70)
Colls.: J. Barnard, F. Garford, H. F. Sewall
Harvey D. Parker Collection   P34

This impression of the *Ecce Homo* is a first state that was not recorded by Meder. It is before the removal of hatching along the right side of the open collar of the pointing soldier. This earlier state was used for the copy of it published by Mommard (see cat. no. 127).

The changes on the block in this subject and in the *Expulsion* (cat. no. 114), as small as they are, probably indicate that Dürer was in close contact with the cutters and printers during the execution of the series.

132. Flagellation of Christ

133. Christ Crowned with Thorns

134. *Ecce Homo*

135. Pilate Washing His Hands

136. Bearing of the Cross

135
Pilate Washing His Hands
1509–1511
From the *Small Passion*
Woodcut, 126 x 99 mm.
B. 36

Meder 145, before the text edition
No visible watermark
Colls.: J. Barnard, F. Garford, H. F. Sewall
Harvey D. Parker Collection   P35

136
Bearing of the Cross
Dated 1509
From the *Small Passion*
Woodcut, 126 x 99 mm.
B. 37

Meder 146, before the text edition
Watermark: Bull's head (M. 70)
Colls.: J. Barnard, F. Garford, H. F. Sewall
Harvey D. Parker Collection   P36

137
Saint Veronica between Saints Peter and Paul
Dated 1510
From the *Small Passion*
Woodcut, 127 x 97 mm.
B. 38

Meder 147, before the text edition
Watermark: Bull's head (M. 70)
Colls.: J. Barnard, F. Garford, H. F. Sewall
Harvey D. Parker Collection   P37

The subject of Saint Veronica standing between Saints
Peter and Paul and holding the Sudarium is not part of the
Passion narrative but is, rather, a devotional subject.
Dürer's use of it in the series is appropriate because, in the
preceding woodcut, she is seen about to wipe Christ's face
as he falls under the weight of the cross. His features were
reputed to have made a permanent imprint on her kerchief, which was afterwards referred to as the Sudarium.

137. Saint Veronica between Saints Peter and Paul

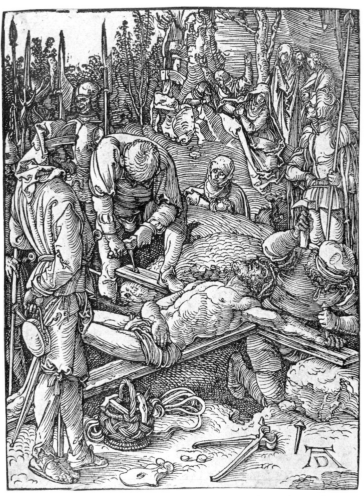

138. Nailing to the Cross

138

Nailing to the Cross

1509–1511
From the *Small Passion*
Woodcut, 126 x 99 mm.
B. 39

Meder 148, before the text edition
No visible watermark
Colls.: J. Barnard, F. Garford, H. F. Sewall
Harvey D. Parker Collection   P38

The cutting of the block for this impression seems to have been less skillful than for most of the others. The hatching is clumsy and lacks variety so that it is difficult to distinguish some of the figures from the landscape. The lamenting women in the background are barely perceptible. This impression bears the damages that Meder ascribes to the 1511 text edition.

139

Crucifixion

1509–1511
From the *Small Passion*
Woodcut, 127 x 97 mm.
B. 40

Meder 149, before the text edition
No visible watermark
Colls.: J. Barnard, F. Garford, H. F. Sewall
Harvey D. Parker Collection   P39

39. Crucifixion

140

Harrowing of Hell

1509–1511
From the *Small Passion*
Woodcut, 126 x 99 mm.
B. 41

Meder 150, after 1511, without text, a–b
No visible watermark
Colls.: J. Barnard, F. Garford, H. F. Sewall
Harvey D. Parker Collection   P40

This is a slightly uneven impression printed after the text edition.

140. Harrowing of Hell

141. Descent from the Cross

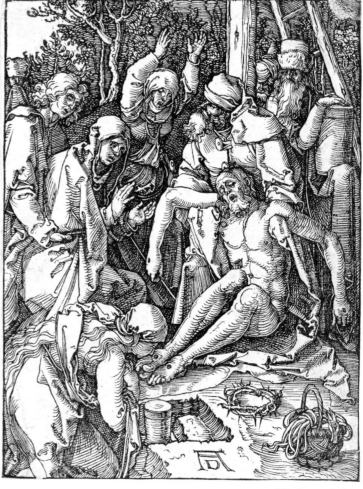

142. Lamentation

141
Descent from the Cross
1509–1511
From the *Small Passion*
Woodcut, 126 x 97 mm.
B. 42

Meder 151, before the text edition
No visible watermark
Colls.: J. Barnard, F. Garford, H. F. Sewall
Harvey D. Parker Collection   P41

142
Lamentation
1509–1511
From the *Small Passion*
Woodcut, 126 x 99 mm.
B. 43

Meder 152, before the text edition
No visible watermark
Colls.: J. Barnard, F. Garford, H. F. Sewall
Harvey D. Parker Collection   P42

The four corners show signs of damages that probably occurred when the print was removed from another sheet to which it had been glued. A portion of the upper right corner is missing, and the lines have been drawn in.

143
Deposition of Christ (Entombment)
1509–1511
From the *Small Passion*
Woodcut, 126 x 97 mm.
B. 44

Meder 153, before the text edition
No visible watermark
Coll.: Tomás Harris
Katherine Eliot Bullard Fund   68.210

The subtle tonal relationships of this very fine, warm early impression make it one of the most attractive of the series exhibited here.

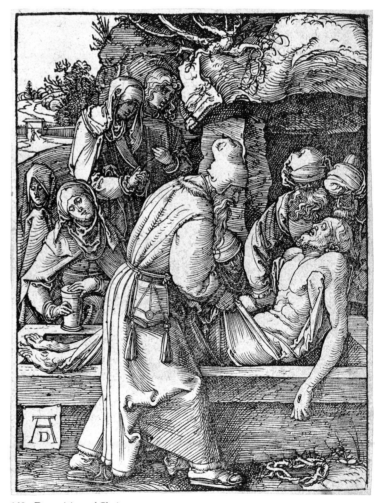

143. Deposition of Christ

144. Resurrection

144
Resurrection
1509–1511
From the *Small Passion*
Woodcut, 126 x 97 mm.
B. 45

Meder 154, before the text edition, a
No visible watermark
Colls.: J. Barnard, F. Garford, H. F. Sewall
Harvey D. Parker Collection   P44

145
Christ Appearing to His Mother
1509–1511
From the *Small Passion*
Woodcut, 124 x 95 mm.
B. 46

Meder 155, after 1511, without text, a
No visible watermark
Colls.: J. Barnard, F. Garford, H. F. Sewall
Harvey D. Parker Collection   P45

In this impression, probably printed after the 1511 text
edition, the figure of Christ and his aureole are well
printed, but the dense shadows behind Mary and in front
of her prayer desk lack clarity.

146
Noli Me Tangere
(Christ Appearing to Mary Magdalen)
1509–1511
From the *Small Passion*
Woodcut, 126 x 99 mm.
B. 47

Meder 156, before the text edition
No visible watermark
Colls.: A. Morrison (Lugt 151), H. Oppenheimer, Tomás
Harris
Gift of William Norton Bullard, by sale of duplicates
68.273

146. *Noli Me Tangere*

145. Christ Appearing to His Mother

147. Christ in Emmaus

148. Christ in Emmaus

147–148

Christ in Emmaus

1509–1511
From the *Small Passion*
Woodcut, 127 x 96 mm.
B. 48

147

Meder 157, before the text edition
Watermark: Bull's head (M. 70)
Coll.: P. Gellatly (Lugt 1185)
Bequest of Francis Bullard   M24879

This is a very fine impression that, unfortunately, has been cut within the arch on three sides.

148

Meder 157, after 1511, without text, a
Watermark: Imperial orb (M. 56)
Colls.: J. Barnard, F. Garford, H. F. Sewall
Harvey D. Parker Collection   P47

Meder dates the watermark about 1530. This impression lacks the delicacy of inking and printing of the earlier one. When the two are compared, one can see how important the architectural framing provided by the archway is to the composition of the print.

149

Doubting Thomas

1509–1511
From the *Small Passion*
Woodcut, 126 x 99 mm.
B. 49

Meder 158, before the text edition
No visible watermark
Colls.: J. Barnard, F. Garford, H. F. Sewall
Harvey D. Parker Collection   P48

149. Doubting Thomas

150. Ascension

151. Pentecost

150
Ascension
1509–1511
From the *Small Passion*
Woodcut, 126 x 97 mm.
B. 50

Meder 159, before the text edition
No visible watermark
Colls.: J. Barnard, F. Garford, H. F. Sewall
Harvey D. Parker Collection   P49

151
Pentecost
1509–1511
From the *Small Passion*
Woodcut, 126 x 97 mm.
B. 51

Meder 160, after 1511, without text, a
No visible watermarks
Colls.: J. Barnard, F. Garford, H. F. Sewall
Harvey D. Parker Collection   P50

Through this impression, probably printed by 1530, it can
be seen that, if printed carefully, impressions after the text
edition are often quite good. At times, they may look even
more attractive than the 1511 edition, simply because the
text on the back does not show through.

152
Last Judgment
1509–1511
From the *Small Passion*
Woodcut, 126 x 97 mm.
B. 52

Meder 161, before the text edition
No visible watermark
Coll.: P. Gellatly (Lugt 1185)
Bequest of Francis Bullard   M24880

152. Last Judgment

153
The School Teacher
Dated 1510
Woodcut, 128 x 97 mm.
B. 133

Meder 267, I, b
Watermark: Bull's head (M. 66)
Coll.: H. A. Cornill-d'Orville (Lugt 529)
William A. Sargent Fund 46.4

In 1510, Dürer produced three broadsheets, each composed of a woodcut accompanied by a poem written by himself. *The School Teacher* humorously illustrates the moralizing text. The cut was reprinted later in the sixteenth century but not with Dürer's verses. Because of the great simplicity of the design and cutting, it is possible that quite late impressions of the woodcut would have printed well, provided the block were carefully inked.

This impression of the broadsheet is incomplete; it lacks the right half, which has two more columns of verse signed with Dürer's monogram. There is an early break in the right borderline.

Wer recht bescheyden wol werden
Der pit got trum hye auff erden

Welcher nit von meiner ler weicht

    Dem würt sein hertz müt vnd syn leicht

Vnd würt alweg in fryden stan

    Gegen im selbs vnd yederman

Offnen nyemandt dein heymlichkeyt

    Auff das dir nit pring rew vnd leydt

Dann man findt also geschriben

    Wenig menschen sind stet bliben

Des menschen gmüt ist wandelbar

    Begerstu fryd noch meim rat var

All pöß nachred vermeyd mit fleyß

    Auff das du drumb erwerfst preyß

Fur kums auch an andrn lewten

    Dye vbls vom negsten bedewten

Solchs stylt deins hertzen grymmikeyt

    Vnd treybt von dir all haß vnd neyd

153. The School Teacher

154–160

LARGE PASSION

1510–1511 (for the subjects completed
earlier, see cat. nos. 47–57)

By 1510, when Dürer made four additional large woodcuts
of Passion subjects, his style had changed considerably
from that evident in the woodcuts designed for the *Large
Passion* at the end of the fifteenth century. Compositions
crowded with detail had given way to a new unity and
harmony. Gone is the strong contrast of angular black lines
on white paper. Fine lines of shading are now cut with
subtle variations in width to create tonal effects, ranging
from pale gray to almost black. The black lines and white
paper now intermix optically to suggest a continuous gray
tone, as if an ink wash had been applied. Large areas of
white paper take on different intensities of brightness
according to the density of black around them. To some
extent, these qualities could be observed in the woodcuts
of the *Small Passion* (cat. nos. 112–152). However, the
change is more obvious in the final group of woodcuts
executed to complete the *Large Passion*. The *Small Passion*
woodblocks of 1509–1511 were, for the most part, cut by
craftsmen of modest ability who often did not succeed in
doing full justice to Dürer's intent, whereas the five woodblocks, including the title page, that complete the *Large
Passion* and the three that finish the *Life of the Virgin*
(cat. nos. 161–165) were cut with greater, and often outstanding, skill.

154–155

Last Supper

Dated 1510
From the *Large Passion*
Woodcut, 396 x 288 mm.
B. 5

154

Meder 114, before the text edition
Watermark: Monogram of Mary (M. 316)
Coll.: R. Fisher (Lugt 2204)
Bequest of Francis Bullard   M24867

In this early impression of the *Last Supper*, the ink, which
seems to be lighter in color than the rich black used for the
earlier subjects (see *Agony in the Garden*, cat. no. 47), has
been applied to the block with great care. The impression
is even, balanced, and restrained in effect, imparting a
sense of calm and serenity to the scene.

Although the impression is early, breaks in the block are
already visible in the central part of the arch and in the
lower borderline at the right corner. The borderline break
has been filled in, probably with an iron gall ink, which
usually turns brown with age. The same color ink is visible
on the feet under the table to the right of its support.

The figure in the left foreground with the pitcher is not
an apostle, but the innkeeper. He is balanced in the right
foreground by Judas, giving the composition a double
arch shape in which the architecture reinforces the grouping of the figures.

155

Meder 114, before the text edition
Watermark: Monogram of Mary (M. 316)
Coll.: Tomás Harris
Stephen Bullard Memorial Fund   68.241

This impression of the *Last Supper* is equally early, but its
general effect is quite different from the preceding. The ink
was applied to the block more generously and appears to
be blacker and denser. There are many light smudges of
ink along and between the printed lines, which may have
resulted when the freshly printed impression was not
pulled neatly from the block. Because the contrast of ink to
paper is stronger in this impression, Christ's head surrounded by light and the figure of Judas assume a greater
significance, thus emphasizing the dramatic tension
between the two figures. Whereas in the preceding impression the vaulting balanced the figures, here, because of
the heavy inking, the figures are more strongly modeled
and seem weightier and the architecture is correspondingly
less important.

The heavier inking, in addition, causes some parts of the
design to read less clearly. The damage in the arch has
been filled in with pen and ink. Otherwise it is a fine impression, equal in quality to the preceding one.

154. Last Supper (reduced)

155. Last Supper (reduced)

156

Betrayal of Christ
Dated 1510
From the *Large Passion*
Woodcut, 397 x 279 mm.
B. 7

Meder 116, before the text edition
Watermark: Monogram of Mary (M. 316)
Coll.: R. Fisher (Lugt 2204)
Bequest of Francis Bullard   M24869

This impression, as the second *Last Supper* (cat. no. 155), is strongly inked, though with greater care; and it has the same dramatic character. The middle gray tone of the background not only describes the darkness, but also unifies the composition.

157

Harrowing of Hell (Christ in Limbo)
Dated 1510
From the *Large Passion*
Woodcut, 396 x 284 mm.
B. 14

Meder 121, before the text edition, b
Watermark: Monogram of Mary (M. 316)
Coll.: R. Fisher (Lugt 2204)
Bequest of Francis Bullard   M24877

The *Harrowing of Hell* may be the first of Dürer's woodcuts executed in 1510 to complete the *Large Passion* series. The problem of using parallel lines to suggest both the tone that describes light and shade and the tone that models forms, has not been fully resolved. There is a confusion between the rays of Christ's aureole and the surface of the wall to his right. The curving, vertical hatching in the background was intended to represent smoke and shadow above sheets of white flame. The prominence of the lines behind the arch prevents them from serving this purpose, and they give, instead, the impression of hanging moss. Therefore, the white area below tends to read, not as flames, but as negative space. It is very likely that the cutter of this block had difficulty adapting to Dürer's new and very sophisticated woodcut style.

The impression is a very fine one, with a unified silvery effect created by the limited range of gray tones.

158

Resurrection
Dated 1510
From the *Large Passion*
Woodcut, 389 x 276 mm.
B. 15

Meder 124, before the text edition
Watermark: Monogram of Mary (M. 316)
Coll.: R. Fisher (Lugt 2204)
Bequest of Francis Bullard   M24878

This is a fine, clear impression printed just before the text edition of 1511. The tonal contrasts are strong, as in the second, more dramatic impression of the *Last Supper* (cat. no. 155). It is lightly foxed all over.

156. Betrayal of Christ (reduced)

157. Harrowing of Hell (reduced)

158. Resurrection (reduced)

159–160

Man of Sorrows, Mocked by a Soldier
Toward 1511
Title page of the *Large Passion*
Woodcut, 232 x 193 mm.
B. 4

159

Meder 113, before the text edition
No visible watermark
Coll.: Tomás Harris
Stephen Bullard Memorial Fund   68.240

The title page of the *Large Passion,* as well as those for the *Apocalypse* (cat. no. 166) and the *Life of the Virgin* (cat. nos. 164, 165) was executed shortly before the three books were published in 1511.

The concept of a Perpetual Passion, in which Christ continues to suffer for the sins of mankind after his Passion on earth ended, was popular in Dürer's time. Here, Dürer transforms the traditional motifs of the mocking soldier and Christ crowned with thorns into a vision in which Christ, with the wounds of the crucifixion visible on his body, is still mocked by man.

There is in the Ashmolean Museum, Oxford, a trial proof of the first state of this woodcut, in which the rays above Christ's head have not been cut back to his crown of thorns. In the British Museum, London, there is a unique impression of the *Man of Sorrows, Mocked by a Soldier* printed very close together on the same sheet with the title page of the *Life of the Virgin* (see cat. no. 164). The impression of the *Man of Sorrows* exhibited has fragments of lines along the left edge of the sheet which belong to the *Life of the Virgin* title page. A few additional impressions of both prints show similar fragments of lines. The fact that these woodcuts were printed as a pair suggests that they were executed at the same time.

This early impression is rare. It is in excellent condition, and the finely cut lines are clearly printed.

160

Meder 113, 1511 edition with Latin text
No visible watermark
Coll.: Tomás Harris
Gift of Horatio G. Curtis, by sale of duplicates   68.248

On the title page of the 1511 edition, verses added by Benedictus Chelidonius beneath the image confirm the eternal suffering of Christ.
These cruel wounds I bear for thee, O man,
And cure thy mortal sickness with my blood.
I take away thy sores with mine, thy death
With mine — a God Who changed to man for thee.
But thou, ingrate, still stabb'st my wounds with sins;
I still take floggings for thy guilty acts.
It should have been enough to suffer once
From hostile Jews; now, friend, let there be peace!
(Panofsky, vol. I, p. 139).

Printed on coarser paper, this impression reads with less clarity than the fine preceding example. Because the series of parallel lines is not clear and crisp, the subtle tonal balance is diminished. The imprint of the text on the verso is visible through the paper and blurs the impression of the text lines below the image.

159. Man of Sorrows, Mocked by a Soldier, title page woodcut (reduced)

Passio domini nostri Jesu. ex hierony-

mo Paduano. Dominico Mancino. Sedulio. et Bapti-
sta Mantuano. per fratrem Chelidonium colle-
cta. cum figuris Alberti Dureri
Norici Pictoris.

Has ego crudeles homo pro te perfero plagas

Atq; meo morbos sanguine curo tuos.

Vulneribusq; meis tua vulnera.morteq; mortem

Tollo deus:pro te plasmate factus homo.

Tuq; ingrate mihi:pungis mea stigmata culpis

Sæpe tuis.noxa vapulo sæpe tua.

Sat fuerit.me tanta olim tormenta sub hoste

Iudæo passum:nunc sit amice quies.

160. Man of Sorrows, Mocked by a Soldier, title page (reduced)

161. Death of the Virgin (reduced)

161
Death of the Virgin
Dated 1510
From the *Life of the Virgin*
Woodcut, 290 x 206 mm.
B. 93

Meder 205, before the text edition, a
Watermark: High crown (M. 20)
Maria Antoinette Evans Fund   M32090

Dürer, after an interval of five or six years, completed the *Life of the Virgin* with two additional subjects and a title page. As in the five later woodcuts of the *Large Passion* (cat. nos. 154–160), the forms are described in terms of parallel shading or modeling lines of relatively uniform width, accompanied by a greater clarity in spatial relationships. The tonal range is more limited and more carefully gradated and textures are more generalized than in the earlier subjects of the series (cat. nos. 63–82).

Every element of the composition now focuses on the central motif — the figure of the dying Virgin. Dürer's exploration of linear perspective, almost an end in itself in earlier prints, such as the *Birth of the Virgin* (cat. nos. 67, 68), now serves to promote the expressive meaning of the whole. If the perspective lines were extended, they would converge just above the Virgin's head. The central figures — the Virgin, Saint John placing a candle in her hand, the priest sprinkling holy water, and Saint Peter kneeling close by her — are isolated from the other apostles by carefully calculated framing devices, such as the strong vertical of the cross.

This is a very good impression except for blotches of printer's ink and the filling in of the extremely fine cross-hatching around the doorway at the right. However, by 1510 the overall lucidity of Dürer's designs, conceived in terms of tonal values, made them less dependent on the clear printing of individual lines with the result that these small imperfections are less disturbing than they would be in the subjects of the *Life of the Virgin* executed earlier.

162–163
Assumption and Coronation of the Virgin
Dated 1510
From the *Life of the Virgin*
Woodcut, 289 x 207 mm.
B. 94

162
Meder 206, before the text edition
Watermark: High crown (M. 20)
Maria Antoinette Evans Fund   M32091

Dürer's solution to the challenging problem of depicting in the same composition the earthly figures of the apostles surrounding the Virgin's empty tomb and the unearthly event of her Coronation is very successful. The figures of Christ, God, and the Virgin, suffused in light, are seen in relief against a shallow segment of heaven. In contradistinction, the world in which the apostles stand recedes into a shadowy distance that is densely cross-hatched. The three apostles in the foreground help to unify the disparate halves of the composition by reiterating the three heavenly figures above.

There is considerable unevenness in the printing. Clogged lines exaggerate the darkness of the scene below.

163
Meder 206, after 1511, without text, c
Watermark: Württemberg arms (M. 188)
Coll.: Tomás Harris
Harvey D. Parker Fund   68.263

This impression, with a watermark Meder dates about 1580–1590, is from a posthumous edition of surprisingly good quality. A sensitive printer has produced a lightly inked and clear impression. The paper, however, has darkened, so that the distinction between the tonal qualities of the upper and lower portions of the print are lost.

162. Assumption and Coronation of the Virgin (reduced)

163. Assumption and Coronation of the Virgin (reduced)

164–165

Madonna on the Crescent

Toward 1511
Title page of the *Life of the Virgin*
Woodcut, 203 x 196 mm.
B. 76

164

Meder 188, before the text edition
Watermark: Bull's head with cross and flower (M. 66)
Maria Antoinette Evans Fund   M32092

In his title page for the *Large Passion* (cat. nos. 159, 160), Dürer adapted a familiar pictorial representation of the Mocking of Christ on earth and gave it a different and more universal meaning. In this title page, Dürer combined two equally familiar representations of the Virgin: the Virgin of Humility, who sits close to the ground holding her infant, as in *The Virgin Mary Roundel* (cat. no. 201), and the divine Virgin crowned with stars who stands on the crescent moon, as in *The Virgin on the Crescent* (cat. no. 197). In the same way that the *Life of the Virgin* was concerned with her human and heavenly roles, so Dürer united these two aspects in the title page to the book. Through the use of celestial images, the humble subject of the Madonna nursing her child is elevated to a heavenly plane.

It was suggested in the nineteenth century that the areas on either side of the bolster might be the curly hair and bristly chin of the "man in the moon" (Dr. Alfred von Sallet, as cited by S. R. Koehler in Museum of Fine Arts, Boston, *Exhibition of Albert Dürer's Engravings, Etchings, Dry-points, and Most of the Woodcuts Executed from His Designs* [Boston, 1888], p. 52, no. 157).

The superb printing on a warm-toned paper produces a glowing light that can only be completely comprehended in a brilliant impression such as this one.

165

Meder 188, 1511 edition with Latin text
No visible watermark
Coll.: Tomás Harris
Katherine Eliot Bullard Fund   68.213

The lines have thickened and small flecks of ink now mar their clarity. The bold type above and the verses below have slightly crowded the Madonna and Child making the image appear earthbound.

166

The Virgin Mary Appearing to Saint John on Patmos

Toward 1511
Title page from the *Apocalypse*
Woodcut, 184 x 182 mm.
B. 60

Meder 163, 1511 edition with Latin text, b
Watermark: Tower with crown and flower (M. 259)
Bequest of William P. Babcock   B95

When Dürer reprinted the *Apocalypse* blocks (cat. nos. 28–46) in 1511 for a new Latin edition, he added a woodcut to the title page that had previously been adorned only with the title, *Apocalipsis cū figuris,* cut in elaborate Gothic letters. Even though the paper is coarse and the text on the verso shows through, this impression of the new woodcut is fine and sharp and displays the freshness of a block recently cut. There is a unique proof from the Barlow Collection in the National Gallery of Australia, Melbourne, in which the rays above the Virgin's head are almost uniform in length. There are also a few rare impressions of the print without the letter block.

The subject of the woodcut, the Virgin and Child appearing in a vision to Saint John on the island of Patmos as he writes his text, is a traditional one. Unlike the revelations of Saint John, it is not a part of the New Testament.

164. Madonna on the Crescent, title page woodcut (reduced)

EPITOME IN DIVAE PARTHENICES MARI AE HISTORIAM AB ALBERTO DVRERO NORICO PER FIGVRAS DIGES TAM CVM VERSIBVS ANNE XIS CHELIDONII

Quifquis fortunæ correptus turbine.perfers
Quam tibi iacturam fata finiftra ferunt.
Aut animæ delicta gemis.Phlegethontis & ignes
Anxius æternos corde tremente paues.
Quifquis & vrgeris iam iam decedere vita
Alterius:migrans:nefcius hofpitij.
Huc ades:auxilium:pete:continuoq; rogabo
Pro te:quem paui lacte:tuliq; finu.
Ille deus rerum mihi fubdidit aftra:deofq;
Flectitur ille meis O homo fupplicijs.

165. Madonna on the Crescent, title page (reduced)

166. The Virgin Mary Appearing to Saint John on Patmos, title page

167–168

The Mass of Saint Gregory
Dated 1511
Woodcut, 300 x 205 mm.
B. 123

167

Meder 226a
Watermark: High crown (M. 20)
Colls.: J. St. Aubyn (Lugt 1534); R. Gutekunst (Lugt 2213a)
Stephen Bullard Memorial Fund   M28699

The year 1511 was a high point in Dürer's production of woodcuts. In addition to issuing his "Three Large Books" and the *Small Passion*, he executed a number of single-sheet woodcuts. In these last, he achieved the mastery of designing woodcuts toward which he was working in the 1510 subjects of the *Large Passion* (cat. nos. 154–160) and the *Life of the Virgin* (cat. nos. 161–165). In the 1510 prints, the uniformity of the lines—long, horizontal parallels; short, more sparsely placed diagonals; and dense cross-hatching—had a unifying effect on all elements of the composition. Yet there were new problems for the cutter, as seen in the *Harrowing of Hell* of the *Large Passion* (cat. no. 157) or in the *Nailing to the Cross* of the *Small Passion* (cat. no. 138). It is evident that by 1511, skilled professional cutters could follow Dürer's designs with ease and without confusion about the meaning or purpose of a single line, for it was no longer important that they reproduce the highly individual character of specific lines.

In Dürer's early woodcuts, such as the *Hercules* (cat. no. 17), the lines are imbued with their own life and calligraphic beauty. Even in 1510, in a woodcut such as the *Betrayal of Christ* (cat. no. 156) from the *Large Passion*, the outlines of forms retain a certain expressiveness, whereas in the *Mass of Saint Gregory*, they have even less variety and exist as integral parts of a harmonious whole. The tonal range in the *Mass of Saint Gregory* is quite wide, but with very subtle transitions between the tones. There is a fluidity in the transitions similar to that found in paintings in "grisaille" (gray monochrome). This tonal painterly effect, in which the figures take on increased volume, has resulted because outlines now dissolve into the surrounding shadows.

In this impression, the use of a deep black ink insures that the most densely cross-hatched areas, such as the shadows behind Christ, contrast strongly with the highlighted portions, such as those of his body. These heightened effects of illumination are most appropriate to the dramatic, revelatory nature of the event. When an attendant at one of Pope Gregory's masses doubted the presence of Christ in the Eucharist, Christ, surrounded by instruments of his Passion, miraculously appeared upon the altar.

This impression is extremely clear and strong. It has been heavily inked, as evidenced by the filling in of the cross-hatching to the left of Christ. Because the tonal relationships have been carefully established in the cutting of the block and maintained in the printing, there is no confusion about the placement and location of the figures and objects within the space of the image. Unfortunately, the collector's mark of J. St. Aubyn was rather conspicuously placed next to the block with Dürer's monogram.

168

Meder 226e–f
Watermark: Urn with star (M. 168)
Coll.: H. F. Sewall (Lugt 1309)
Harvey D. Parker Collection   P160

According to Meder's dating of the watermark, this impression of the *Mass of Saint Gregory* was printed slightly after the middle of the sixteenth century. Its unattractive appearance is the result of the discoloration of the paper and uneven inking and printing, as much as it is due to the somewhat worn condition of the block. With Dürer's new woodcut style, the manner in which the block deteriorated differed from that of the earlier blocks. The second impression of the *Holy Family with Three Hares* (cat. no. 20) was printed in the second half of the sixteenth century; and it is interesting to compare the two late impressions and to observe how the deterioration of a block from about 1497 and a 1511 block has affected the expressive qualities of each impression in a different way.

The block for the *Mass of Saint Gregory*, besides those for the other prints after 1500, does not display the large cracks that so often occur in later impressions of the early woodblocks. It may be that the smaller blocks he often used after 1500 were less cumbersome, less susceptible to warping; also, they may have been of one piece of wood rather than two pieces joined.

The straight and regular lines in Dürer's new woodcut style, in spite of their comparative fineness, did not break as easily as the uneven, curving, or angular lines of the early blocks. The *Small Passion* blocks in the British Museum suggest that for the new style, it was no longer necessary to cut the grooves as deeply; therefore, the raised lines are less apt to break away than those in the earlier, deeply cut woodblocks. Because, by 1510, Dürer's backgrounds are filled with shading, the printing surface

167. The Mass of Saint Gregory (reduced)

168. The Mass of Saint Gregory (reduced)

of the block was necessarily more level and better able to withstand pressure. When breaks did occur, as is seen here in the horizontal hatching of the shadows at top right, the loss to the image, conceived in terms of areas of tone rather than individual, descriptive lines, was not as crucial.

In the *Mass of Saint Gregory*, the broadening of the lines through wear is more detrimental to the quality of the impression than any other factor. The volume of the figures is disturbed; they flatten and occupy less space. Edges of forms, such as the clouds and the uplifted arm of the attendant with the censer, which in the early impression of this print seemed to melt into the shadows, now have hard outlines. Because the dense cross-hatching has worn, the background shadows are less transparent, and the illusion of space behind the background figures is absent.

On the other hand, the broadening of lines in the *Holy Family with Three Hares* affected first the clarity of details. There is also a loss of depth, but it is a secondary effect, the result of illegibility of details and the confusion of planes, rather than the compression of continuous space.

169
The Trinity
Dated 1511
Woodcut, 391 x 285 mm.
B. 122

Meder 187b–c
Watermark: Crown (similar to M. 35)
Bequest of Francis Bullard   M24896

The Trinity is Dürer's largest and perhaps the most completely successful woodcut of the many dated 1511. This beautiful impression, trimmed just within most of the borderline, is otherwise in excellent condition. However, it probably is not among the earliest impressions, according to Meder's description of the watermarks and inking. The Crown is a variant of a watermark cited for another impression printed about 1520. Because most of the borderline is lacking, Meder's description of progressive breaks is not of assistance. He describes early impressions of this woodcut as being printed in a rather dark black ink that would give it a range of contrasts similar to the *Mass of Saint Gregory* (cat. no. 167). Here, the warm tone of the paper is in key with the somewhat grayish ink. The pale ink, when applied to the very fine parallel lines that shade both the background and the figures, creates an overall silvery tonality. Dürer may have had the block reprinted so that he could take a number of impressions to sell in the Netherlands.

Like the three title pages to the large woodcut series (cat. nos. 159, 164, 166), the *Trinity* appears as a supernatural vision. God the Father, Christ, and the Holy Spirit, surrounded by angels and the instruments of Christ's Passion, are seen on a heavenly level above the Four Winds. The disposition of the figures in the *Trinity* is identified iconographically as a Throne of Mercy. Instead of God the Father holding Christ nailed to a cross, he supports his son, the Man of Sorrows.

The Museum of Fine Arts owns a drawing by Dürer dated 1515 in which he simplified and revised the composition (W. 583).

169. The Trinity (reduced)

170. Adoration of the Magi (reduced)

170

Adoration of the Magi
Dated 1511
Woodcut, 295 x 221 mm.
B. 3

Meder 208a
Watermark: Bull's head (M. 70)
Katherine Eliot Bullard Fund   1971.71

This is an exceptionally beautiful and early impression.
A small break on the underside of the broad beam in the
foreground has been filled in. A comparison of the print
with the woodcut of the same subject from the *Life of the
Virgin* (cat. no. 76), executed about eight years earlier,
demonstrates further aspects of the change in Dürer's
woodcut style. Each design, to be wholly successful, demanded a cutter of great skill. In the earlier print, the cutter
was required to represent a multitude of contrasting
textures that ornament and enhance the design; the 1511
cutter was required to represent only those textural objects
that play a functional part in the composition. In the earlier
print, a diffuse light played impartially on a wealth of
detail. In 1511, the scene is illuminated from the left, and
the light emphasizes the volume of the figures. In the
Adoration from the *Life of the Virgin*, the imaginative
architecture was not always subordinate to the subject.
Here the columns and beams of the porch with thatched
roof have a major expressive function. They add solidity to
the composition and establish a scale that gives a classic
monumentality to the figures.

171

Saint Jerome in His Cell
Dated 1511
Woodcut, 236 x 160 mm.
B. 114

Meder 228a
No visible watermark
Coll.: H. S. Theobald (Lugt 1375)
Bequest of Francis Bullard   M24894

Saint Jerome, who lived from about 347 to 419 or 420, was
both a great scholar and a wise, intelligent critic. It was he
who translated the Bible into Latin, excluding such
apocryphal texts as the Book of James.

The rational perspective, the judicious placement of the
furnishings of the room, and the expressive light in this
woodcut foreshadow the extraordinary statement Dürer
was to make in the 1514 engraving of the same subject
(cat. no. 186). The woodcut, however, is necessarily less
ambitious than the engraving in its attempt to depict
variety of detail, which can be much more effectively performed with a burin. Furthermore, Dürer's new woodcut
style engendered a subordination of the specific character
of surface textures to the subtle description of volumes.

The directness and strength of this fine impression stem
from a simple contrast between the broad white areas of
the curtain, the lion, and Saint Jerome's cloak and the areas
shadowed by parallel hatching. The curtain seems to have
been drawn aside to reveal to the viewer the saint at work
in the privacy of his study.

171. Saint Jerome in His Cell

172–174

Saint Jerome in a Cave
Dated 1512
Woodcut, 169 x 124 mm.
B. 113

172

Meder 229, I, a
Watermark: Bull's head with serpent (M. 81)
Coll.: H. S. Theobald (Lugt 1375)
Samuel Putnam Avery Fund   M28550

The small *Saint Jerome in a Cave* is an important departure
from the 1511 woodcuts. Forms are defined in terms of
planes shaded with very thin parallel lines and almost no
cross-hatching. The tonal scale is reduced to a bare minimum. Space and volume are only suggested by the juxta-
position of groups of parallel lines, and there is virtually no
description of specific textures. All these factors have their
effect on the composition. The surface pattern predomi-
nates, but in a manner that is totally different from Dürer's
calligraphic fifteenth-century woodcuts. Saint Jerome and
the lion are not given special emphasis but are integrated
with the landscape.

This is a brilliant impression characterized by great
clarity owing to the fineness of the lines and the skillful
inking and printing.

173

Meder 229, I, C, c, without text
No visible watermark
Coll.: H. F. Sewall (Lugt 1309)
Harvey D. Parker Collection   P150

In 1514, the *Saint Jerome in a Cave* woodcut was used as a
title page to Bishop Eusebius' *Life of Saint Jerome* published
in Nuremberg by H. Hölzel. After that, the print was
again issued without text. This impression, according to
Meder, can be dated about 1560–1580. Breaks are visible,
for example, on the horizon line near the crucifix and
in the top borderline toward the right. Although the lines
have broadened slightly, the heaviness of the impression
is the result of the block having been overinked. The discolored paper detracts from the effect of sunlight seen in
the preceding impression. All of the delicacy and clarity of
the earlier impression has been lost.

174

Meder 229, II, b
Date 1512, removed
Watermark: Double-headed eagle (similar to M. 227)
Coll.: H. F. Sewall (Lugt 1309)
Harvey D. Parker Collection   P151

This impression is deceptively good. It would appear to be
earlier than the foregoing if one did not observe that the
break in the horizon line is wider, and the date 1512 had
broken away or was removed (and is here added in pen).
The watermark is a variant of one that Meder dates around
1600.

It is obvious that this impression was issued by an able,
sensitive printer who used a thin ink to recapture what he
could of the print's original clarity, and a fine paper that
responded to Dürer's delicate lines.

The upper right corner of this impression has been replaced and redrawn in pen.

172. Saint Jerome in a Cave

173. Saint Jerome in a Cave

174. Saint Jerome in a Cave

175. Saint Jerome by the Pollard Willow

175–176

Saint Jerome by the Pollard Willow

Dated 1512
Drypoint, 211 x 183 mm.
B. 59

175

Meder 58, II, a
No visible watermark
Coll.: Waldburg Wolfegg (Lugt 2542)
Anna Mitchell Richards Fund   M33780

Dürer executed only three prints in the drypoint medium.
Of these, two are dated 1512 (the present subject and the
Man of Sorrows with Hands Bound, B. 21, not exhibited).
The third, the *Holy Family* (cat. no. 177) is undated but
closely related in style. (For a definition of drypoint and
drypoint burr, see the Glossary.) When Dürer made these
prints, drypoint was a very uncommon medium. The only
drypoints he is likely to have seen were those by the first
printmaker to use the medium, the Housebook Master,
whose style Dürer emulated in one of his earliest engravings, the *Young Woman Attacked by Death* (cat. no. 1). In
Saint Jerome by the Pollard Willow, Dürer exploited further
than the Housebook Master the properties of drypoint burr.

In the present example, one of the finest known impressions of the second state (the very rare first state lacks
Dürer's monogram), the rich burr retains generous amounts
of ink, and prints as softly spreading areas of velvety black
that overflow the lines. Burr softens the lines of the landscape, producing an atmospheric effect comparable to that
seen in contemporary Venetian paintings. Lines with
strong burr occupy the opposite end of the tonal scale from
lines without burr that are scratched into the plate with the
greatest possible delicacy, such as those that delineate the
head of the saint.

Early impressions of this print and of the *Holy Family*
drypoint (cat. no. 177) are often characterized by extensive
use of selective inking and wiping of the plate for expressive purposes. It would indeed have been virtually impossible to wipe the *Saint Jerome* plate clean of all excess
ink because of the manner in which the heavy burr
retains the ink. In this impression, the pattern of inking
and wiping reinforces the solid architectural structure of
the composition. The principal function of this selective
inking and wiping of the plate is, however, to create an
impression of light falling on the scene. The saint's
features have been wiped clean of ink while a very light
film has been left on the rock face above and to the left

175a. Saint Jerome by the Pollard Willow (enlarged detail)

of his head, which serves as a foil for this clean wiping (see detail). As a result, the head and upper body of the praying saint seem to be irradiated by a heavenly light and appear almost transparent.

As in a few other early impressions of the second state, the upper left corner of the plate was masked before printing, cutting off the tips of the blades of grass growing on the rocks below. Traces of the lower edge of the mask are visible as a light indentation of the paper. Ink has accidentally collected along this edge and prints as a blotchy line in the sky above the rocks. The purpose of the masking is not known, but it is very likely that it was used to prevent accidental marks, similar to the fine scratches in the sky around the crucifix, from printing. If these marks had printed, they would have dimmed the brilliant white light that emanates from the upper left. The impression is printed on a somewhat finer, thinner paper than most impressions of Dürer's engravings, etchings, and drypoints. This choice was probably determined by the fragile nature of the drypoint burr and the delicacy of the lines.

The superb quality of this impression is matched by fine condition. The sheet has been clipped along the plate mark with only minimal losses to the design.

176

Meder 58, II, c–d
Watermark: Large city gate (M. 268)
Gift of Richard H. Zinser   M.App.

The drypoint burr standing up on the surface of the plate beside the lines is very fragile and wears down rapidly with repeated printing. The *Saint Jerome* plate could have produced only a few impressions in which the burr was as rich in effect as in the preceding impression. Dürer's drypoint lines were generally shallower and more transient than his engraved or etched lines.

The present impression, with a watermark dating from the second half of the sixteenth century, dramatizes these observations. The image is barely visible. Printing the plate with a grayish tone of ink has further obscured the faint drypoint lines, which no longer have burr. Numerous accidental scratches mar the plate surface. The condition of this sheet is very bad and helps to confuse what remains of the original image; there are brownish glue stains around the edges that are the result of mounting and also creases, folds, tears, and abrasion of the paper surface. The plate was subsequently extensively reworked in a futile attempt to retrieve the image.

176. Saint Jerome by the Pollard Willow

Holy Family with Saint John, the Magdalen, and Nicodemus
Probably 1512
Drypoint, 210 x 181 mm.
B. 43

177

Meder 44, before stroke through Virgin's face, a–b
No visible watermark
Coll.: F. Kalle (Lugt 1021)
Anna Mitchell Richards Fund   M33781

Although not as fine as the *Saint Jerome by the Pollard Willow* (cat. no. 175), an impression of the *Holy Family* of this quality is nevertheless quite uncommon owing to the speed with which the burr disappeared from the drypoint lines. The delicacy of Dürer's drypoint line and the subtle shading produced by the burr made it possible for Dürer to give the Virgin's features a softness unprecedented in printmaking on metal. It is interesting to compare the face of this Virgin (see detail) with the face of the engraved *Madonna on a Grassy Bench* of 1503 (cat. no. 61), in which Dürer sought a comparable feeling of softness and tenderness. The burin, even in the hands of an engraver as skillful and inventive as Dürer, could never duplicate the melting softness of the Virgin's features in the drypoint.

As in the *Saint Jerome* drypoint, the burr is supported by a tone of ink in areas of shadow, and highlights have been strengthened by wiping. Various degrees of wiping and tone of ink are particularly evident in the folds of the Virgin's mantle. A film of tone veils the entire left foreground including the figure of Joseph seated humbly on the ground. Although the use of tone and of wiping is not as specific as in the *Saint Jerome,* it was nonetheless quite carefully considered in areas such as the figure of the Christ Child, whose limbs are partly illuminated by wiping and partly shadowed by tone.

Yellow stains unfortunately intrude into some of the bright, clean wiped areas on the figures of the Virgin and the Magdalen (who stands at the right with her ointment jar), somewhat reducing contrasts. The sheet is clipped on the plate mark.

The presence of John, Mary Magdalen, and Nicodemus, the witnesses of the Passion, serves as a reminder of the tragic events to come.

178

Meder 44, stroke through Virgin's face partly polished away, c
Watermark: Bishop's arms (M. 39)
Colls.: Liechtenstein, Tomás Harris
Harvey D. Parker Fund   68.260

At some point in the plate's career, a diagonal scratch was made across the face of the Virgin. Panofsky believed that Dürer made the scratch himself in order to express his displeasure with the plate. Meder, however, describes an impression without the scratch that has a watermark dated after Dürer's death. One must admit that the idea of "cancelling" a plate by marring it in some fashion in order to prevent its being printed further is a concept that is usually associated with nineteenth-century, rather than sixteenth-century, printmaking. By the time this impression was printed (probably 1600 or after on the basis of Meder's description of the condition of the plate) someone seems to have attempted to diminish the effect of the scratch by polishing it out of the plate. In addition, many of the lines appear to be stronger than in the preceding impression, as, for example, the lines of the Virgin's head and the mantel covering it (see detail). These lines have been reworked by deepening the grooves originally scratched in the plate. On closer examination with magnification, these reworked lines show a ragged contour and much less variety of width than Dürer's original lines. As a result of this reworking, the Virgin's expression has changed: pursed lips have replaced the subtle mobility of her smile.

Some form of corrosion has occurred to the plate and is particularly visible on the three figures standing at the back. An attempt to remove this corrosion from the sky around the figures at the upper right has left many scraping and polishing scratches. A final defect occurred when the paper moved in the press, producing a blurred effect in the lower foreground.

177. Holy Family with Saint John, the Magdalen, and Nicodemus

178. Holy Family with Saint John, the Magdalen, and Nicodemus

177a. Holy Family with Saint John, the Magdalen, and Nicodemus
(enlarged detail)

178a. Holy Family with Saint John, the Magdalen, and Nicodemus
(enlarged detail)

179. Knight, Death, and the Devil

179–182

Knight, Death, and the Devil
Dated 1513
Engraving, 246 x 190 mm.
B. 98

179
Meder 74a
No visible watermark
Coll.: Tomás Harris
Harvey D. Parker Fund   68.261

Like the *Fall of Man* of 1504 (cat. nos. 84–85), this plate is engraved with a multiplicity of detail. Here, however, Dürer does not employ the strong contrast produced by light figures silhouetted against a dark ground seen in the earlier plate. A twilight atmosphere prevails, and in the half darkness a great many intricate details are defined by a much more limited range of intermediate tones. In this shadowy mountain pass, surface textures and ornaments of man, beast, and the supernatural are depicted with extraordinary skill and subtlety.

This fine, early impression is strong and sharply printed in a blue black ink. The plate was wiped clean of excess ink before printing. Aside from a few scratches in the sky, caused by the wiping of the plate, there is no sign of damage. There is a subtle but clearly defined spatial relationship established in the background by the blackness of the thorny tree in the middle distance and the grayness of the distant castle tower, an effect that is missing in the other impressions exhibited.

The subject has been interpreted as a Christian knight, invulnerable in his armor to the rotting corpse of death riding beside him and the horned devil behind. He appears to be riding through the "valley of the shadow of death" toward the light of salvation.

180
Meder 74b(?)
No visible watermark
Bequest of Mrs. Horatio G. Curtis   27.1353

The combination of generous inking and yellowish paper produces a warm, brownish quality in this impression. There are more wiping scratches in the sky than in the preceding impression. Moreover, tiny blotches, apparently caused by corrosion, are evident, most noticeably in the lower right corner (see details). Similar blotches may be seen in the engraved *Hercules* (cat. nos. 15–16). Since corrosion appeared early in the *Hercules* plate, this impres-

sion of *Knight, Death, and the Devil* may also have been taken at an early stage; however it must be later than the preceding, where the damage has not yet occurred.

The castle tower and the thorny tree are equally black, which disturbs the spatial relationship seen in the previous impression. This sameness of tone may be due to the generous inking of the plate.

181
Meder 74d
No visible watermark
Colls.: H. F. Sewall (Lugt 1309)
Gift at the Request of Miss Ellen T. Bullard   59.804

This late impression shows a loss of modeling which produces a thicket of confusing detail and a generally flat and gray appearance. The apparently slight but sensitive differences between tones are needed to define clearly spatial relationships in this print. Surface textures have become less specific so that the sheen of the horse's hide in the early impressions has now become matte and lusterless.

182
Modern facsimile reproduction
Heliogravure by Armand-Durand, Paris.

Like the engraved plate, this facsimile reproduction is produced by an intaglio process, by which the printed lines of ink are raised above the surface of the paper. The image was transferred to a plate by photographic means. Accidental flecks produced by this photomechanical process are visible in white areas such as the sky.

All the lines coarsen; fine lines of hatching, such as those describing the horse's belly, have filled in. The lines tend also to acquire equal values, which results in a more limited tonal range; a noticeable flattening of forms results (see detail).

180. Knight, Death, and the Devil

181. Knight, Death, and the Devil

213

179a. Knight, Death, and the Devil (enlarged detail, before corrosion)

180a. Knight, Death, and the Devil (enlarged detail, with corrosion)

182a. Knight, Death, and the Devil (facsimile reproduction, enlarged detail)

182. Knight, Death, and the Devil (facsimile reproduction)

215

183. The Sudarium Displayed by Two Angels

183

The Sudarium Displayed by Two Angels
Dated 1513
Engraving, 100 x 139 mm.
B. 25

Meder 26b
No visible watermark
Stephen Bullard Memorial Fund   44.820

Represented here by a fine impression, this engraving displays a strict symmetry of composition. The figures are conceived as high reliefs projecting from a neutral background plane, and they are consistently illuminated by a light that enters from the left. Emotion is restrained by the quiet solemnity of the design and finds expression only in the sorrowing faces of the angels and the anguished features of Christ.

    For the Sudarium as a subject, see cat. no. 137.

184

Saint Thomas
Dated 1514
Engraving, 117 x 74 mm.
B. 48

Meder 50b
No visible watermark
Colls.: P. Behaim (Lugt 365), J. Malcolm (Lugt 1780), British Museum duplicate (Lugt 305), Tomás Harris
Centennial Gift of Landon T. Clay   68.190

With this plate and *Saint Paul* (B. 50, not exhibited), Dürer began a series of engravings of the apostles, which he never completed. In 1523 he engraved three more, including the monumental *Saint Philip* (cat. no. 214).

    Dürer's ability to manipulate light in an engraving is especially apparent in a fine, perfectly preserved impression such as this one. The saint's halo generates so brilliant a light that it appears brighter than the blank paper of the background into which it bursts. The treatment of the saint's radiance and his drapery are comparable to that in the *Virgin on the Crescent* of 1516 (cat. no. 197).

    The pose of Saint Thomas' head expresses vividly his attitude of doubt toward the existence of the risen Christ. The lance refers to the wound made in Christ's side and into which Thomas was asked to thrust his hand to convince himself of the reality of the Resurrection.

184. Saint Thomas

185. Madonna by the Wall

185

Madonna by the Wall
Dated 1514
Engraving, 147 x 100 mm.
B. 40

Meder 36, I, b
No visible watermark
Colls.: P. Mariette (Lugt 1790), Friedrich August II (Lugt 971), Tomás Harris
Katherine Eliot Bullard Fund   68.205

The *Madonna by the Wall* may, at first glance, seem to resemble in motif and composition the *Madonna with the Pear* of 1511 (cat. no. 109); but it is, in fact, quite different both in manner of execution and tonal effect. The tonality of the print of 1514 is lighter, more silvery than the engraving of 1511, with its dramatic contrasts of light and dark. The lines themselves are finer and more delicately engraved, and the long sweeping parallel strokes, characteristic of the *Madonna with the Pear,* are here only one of a great variety of combinations of hatchings, cross-hatchings, and stipplings that describe the qualities of varied materials and the shimmering play of light and shadow over their surfaces. This network of fine engraved lines is quite transparent and blends optically with the white of the paper to suggest tone and color. In *Melencolia* (cat. no. 188), executed in the same year, Dürer employed a similar linear vocabulary and tonal range to create a mood very different from the serenity of the *Madonna by the Wall.*

186–187

Saint Jerome in His Study

Dated 1514
Engraving, 248 x 191 mm.
B. 60

186

Meder 59a
No visible watermark
Gift of Mrs. W. Scott Fitz   M29037

In spite of the multitude of meticulously described objects in the room, a sense of order and tranquility prevails. This feeling of peace is achieved partly by the carefully described perspective of the room, which provides a framework for the precise placement of each element whether lion, desk, gourd, or skull. The expressive use of linear perspective, already evident by 1511 in the woodcuts, is nowhere used more sensitively than in this engraving. The repeated circular shapes of gourd, cardinal's hat, and nimbus help to focus attention on the head of the saint.

This brilliant impression must be one of the earliest taken from the plate and is in a pristine state of preservation with wide margins. The most delicate lines print as intended; each value in a tonal range from the palest gray to nearly black, forms part of a balanced relationship. A harmonious and lucid description of the three dimensionality of objects and their location in space is achieved.

The technical and physical perfection of this impression contribute to an expressive mood, created with light, whose warmth and pervasive quality is visible only in very early impressions. One looks into a peaceful interior with a scholar at work. Sunlight enters the windows, is reflected onto ceiling beams, and activates surfaces whether hard stone wall or soft fur. The sunshine is outdone only by the supernatural brilliance of the saint's halo, which is virtually the only area of the plate where the burin has not left its mark and where the white of the paper is untouched.

187

Meder 59b
No visible watermark
Gift of Mrs. Henry P. Kidder   37.353

In comparison with the magnificence of the previous impression, this one, although still good, appears dull and inferior. The grays are too close in value to one another, and the print therefore lacks depth and contrast. In addition, the position in space of objects is no longer clear. The sense of light playing over forms and activating surfaces found in the earlier impression has disappeared, and the saint's halo has lost its brilliance (see details).

The sheet has had a number of small tears along the upper and lower edges mended and retouched with wash, and the paper is rubbed and discolored.

186. Saint Jerome in His Study

187. Saint Jerome in His Study

186a. Saint Jerome in His Study (enlarged detail)

187a. Saint Jerome in His Study (enlarged detail)

188–189

Melencolia I

Dated 1514
Engraving, 243 x 187 mm.
B. 74

188

Meder 75, II, b–c
No visible watermark
Coll.: Ch. S. Bale (Lugt 640)
Gift of Miss Ellen T. Bullard   59.805

The cool black ink and cleanly printed lines of this fine impression enable one to assess further the narrowing range of contrasts of light and shade in Dürer's engravings. On only a very few areas, principally the sphere, drapery, and title, has the white of the paper been left untouched. The plate has been hatched, stippled, or otherwise engraved over most of its surface to print in an apparently infinite range of gray tones.

The impression is a second state, indicated by the correction of the numeral 9 in the square below the bell. The change was made very early so that impressions of the second state can be as fine as the extremely rare first state.

A massive female figure sits brooding among the tools of architecture and carpentry. The meaning of this print has been discussed at length by Panofsky (vol. I, pp. 156–171). He sees in the print various complex and interlocking concepts, both literary and visual, that relate to the "black humor," Melancholy, and to the Liberal Art of Geometry. To Panofsky, this powerful image would appear to express the temperamental difficulties of the intellectual artist, in this instance, Dürer himself.

189

Meder 75, II, b–c
No visible watermark
Colls.: P. Lely (Lugt 2092), Tomás Harris
Centennial Gift of Landon T. Clay   68.188

This is a richly inked impression, printed on a warm yellowish paper. It exaggerates the limited contrasts of light and shade and points up the dramatic lighting. The darkness of the winged woman's face accentuates her brooding expression.

The lines of the right-hand two-thirds of the print are thicker and darker than those of the left. This probably happened during printing. The felts used for padding in the press may have slipped off the left side, subjecting the right side to greater pressure.

It is difficult to ascertain to which Meder category this and the previous impression belong. Neither sheet has a watermark, but both papers have very similar characteristics.

Moreover, Meder's discussion of scratches on the plate is unreliable. It has been pointed out by Carlene Soller, formerly on the Museum staff, and Richard Field, of the Philadelphia Museum of Art, respectively, that the scratch from the bat's tail through the water and the horizontal scratch on the woman's thigh (which Meder ascribes to later printings of the second state) are perfectly visible in the first state. The two impressions differ in nuances of light and shadow, in emphasis, and in coloration. Dürer himself seems to have printed the plate both ways: richly inked and brownish, lightly inked and silvery. Both kinds are to be found in a range of impressions which could be categorized as fine to good.

Peter Lely's collector's mark and inventory number appear on this impression as well as on an impression of the *Prodigal Son* (cat. no. 3).

188. Melencolia I

189. Melencolia I

190
Man of Sorrows Seated
Dated 1515
Etching, 110 x 65 mm.
B. 22

Meder 22, I, c
No visible watermark
Colls.: Liechtenstein, Tomás Harris
Gift of Landon T. Clay and Guido R. Perera   68.198

This is believed by many authorities to be the earliest of
Dürer's six etchings (for a discussion of etching, see the
Introduction and Glossary). Its modest size and the tenta-
tive, halting character of its execution support this opinion.
The lack of certainty in the etched line is very evident
when the *Man of Sorrows* is compared with another etching of 1515, the *Agony in the Garden* (cat. no. 191), in which
the lines are decisive and strong throughout (see details).
The head of the *Man of Sorrows* with its confused tangle of
lines provides the most telling example of Dürer's initial
difficulties with the new medium. There are also signs in
this area that something went amiss in the biting of the
plate that caused the lines to run together, producing a
clotted effect.

All of Dürer's etchings, and, indeed, most German etchings that can be dated prior to the mid-sixteenth century,
seem to have been executed on hammered iron or steel
plates. These were more vulnerable than copper plates to
rusting and corrosion of the plate surface. In this impression, some rust spots have already appeared; note, for
example, the gray flecks on the shoulders and chest of
Christ. Someone has attempted to minimize the effect of a
rust spot near Christ's left elbow by scraping the surface
of the paper.

190. Man of Sorrows Seated

190a. Man of Sorrows Seated (enlarged detail)

191. Agony in the Garden

191–192

Agony in the Garden
Dated 1515
Etching, 225 x 160 mm.
B. 19

191
Meder 19, before rust marks, a–c
Watermark: Letter B (M. 291)
Colls.: Friedrich August II (Lugt 971), Tomás Harris
Katherine Eliot Bullard Fund   68.206

Three of Dürer's etchings on iron or steel (this print, the *Sudarium*, cat. no. 193, and the *Abduction*, cat. no. 194) are characterized by crackling energy of line and intensely dramatic contrasts of light and shadow.

While the engraver's burin demanded great discipline and control, the etching needle traced lines in the ground covering the plate with a freedom comparable to drawing with pen and ink on paper. Dürer's etched lines did not, however, vary in thickness and strength in the manner of his pen lines. The blunt strength of the bitten line was reinforced by the nature of the printer's ink that was, unlike the thin, transparent inks Dürer used for pen drawings, concentrated and opaque.

For this impression the plate was selectively wiped, leaving a tone of ink in certain areas. A film of ink strengthens the shading of Christ's cloak and casts a shadow over the shrubbery and the tree trunk behind him. Although this pattern of tonal inking is very broad, it serves to intensify the light that emanates from the head of Christ. The inking and wiping of the plate focuses attention not only on the figure of Christ, but also picks out Judas and the soldiers entering through the gate of the garden in the distance.

Most of the impressions of Dürer's etchings exhibited here show evidence of technical difficulties in wiping the plate. The ink has often been pulled accidentally from the etched line during the wiping process, producing random streaks and blurs that can be easily mistaken for scratches or rust marks; notice, for example, the curving streak of ink in the dark sky above the gate and the streaky blurs of ink on the ground in front of the gate. Perhaps the breadth of the channel bitten in the plate made it difficult to wipe the plate without pulling ink from the lines.

Although this is an impression of the highest quality, someone has attempted to make the edges of the plate seem more heavily inked. The plate mark has been considerably strengthened by numerous retouchings with brush, and a film of tone has been suggested with gray wash that has been brushed in at certain points between the borderline and the plate mark.

192
Meder 19, with rust marks, b
No visible watermark
Coll.: H. F. Sewall (Lugt 1309)
Harvey D. Parker Collection   P281

In this late impression from the worn plate, the light that flared out in the darkness in the earlier impression is replaced by an overall grayness. This is not merely the product of wear and poor printing but is, in large measure, a result of the extensive corrosion of the iron or steel plate. The fine pits in the plate's surface caused by rust or other corrosion retain ink and print as a gray tone. Numerous scratches around the monogram and date seem to indicate an attempt to remove rust marks from this area of the plate.

Not only is this impression printed from a worn, corroded plate, but it is also poorly preserved. The sheet has been clipped on the borderline inside the plate mark and several wormholes in the paper have been repaired with patches applied from the back and the missing lines drawn in with pen and ink (as, for example, in the rays above Christ's forehead).

191a. Agony in the Garden (enlarged detail)

192. Agony in the Garden

193

The Sudarium Spread Out by an Angel
Dated 1516
Etching, 185 x 135 mm.
B. 26

Meder 27, before rust marks, c
No visible watermark
Coll.: H. F. Sewall (Lugt 1309)
Harvey D. Parker Collection   P289

Three years earlier, in 1513, Dürer had treated the subject
of the Sudarium displayed by angels in an engraving
(cat. no. 183). The engraving is characterized by symmetry
of composition, consistent illumination, and emotional
restraint.

The etching of 1516 is, on the contrary, charged with
emotional excitement. The whole image seems to be
agitated by a great wind. The subtle tonal gradations and
rational illumination of the engraving are replaced by
abrupt contrasts and flickering highlights, which demate-
rialize forms and lend mystery to them. The kerchief with
Christ's face imprinted on it is lifted by the wind like a flag
and seems to extend beyond the borderline. Christ's image
is in deep shadow and it is the angel's upturned gaze
that directs attention to it.

According to Meder's catalogue, this impression should
date from the mid-sixteenth century. It has all the vertical
scratches (visible on the left wing of the angel and the
clouds at lower right) that he describes for other impressions he had seen on paper with a watermark he dates
roughly 1540–1565.

Since the rust marks seem to have formed quite early on
certain of the iron or steel etching plates (the *Man of
Sorrows Seated,* cat. no. 190, and the *Landscape with the
Cannon,* cat. no. 198, for example) it would be natural to
assume that all impressions without rust marks are early
ones. However, if one reads Meder's catalogue carefully,
one discovers that for other etched plates there are impressions that lack rust marks but were printed after Dürer's
death. These are dated by Meder on the basis of their
watermarks. The Museum owns, for example, another fine
impression before rust marks of the *Agony in the Garden,*
which has a watermark that dates from the mid-sixteenth
century.

Whoever had these etching plates in their possession
must have been taking good care of them, keeping them
greased, when not in use, in the same way that armor was
greased to protect it from rust. It is probable that the iron
or steel plates withstood the pressure of repeated printing
better than the copper plates Dürer used for his engravings
and were, therefore, capable of producing good, clear impressions for a longer time. Furthermore, the breadth of
Dürer's etched line and the relative simplicity of his
etched designs meant that these images would be less
readily affected by the wearing of the plate than would his
engraved plates, with their greater variety of line and more
complex designs.

193. The Sudarium Spread Out by an Angel

194–196

The Abduction

Dated 1516
Etching, 310 x 215 mm.
B. 72

194

Meder 67, before rust marks
Watermark: Anchor in circle (similar to M. 171)
Colls.: Yorck von Wartenburg (Lugt 2669), Tomás Harris
Katherine Eliot Bullard Fund   68.208

The *Abduction* is full of impetuous movement. This sense
of motion is not the result of accurate notation of human
and animal movement, for the shaggy unicorn rears up on
its hind legs following a contemporary convention used to
represent a horse at a gallop, and the abducted girl flings
her arms out in a wooden gesture of despair. The sense of
motion stems, rather, from Dürer's dynamic use of line and
of patterns of light and shadow to animate the image. A
series of concentric curving lines radiate from the lower
torso of the abductor, giving the figures a spiraling motion.
Even the lines of the landscape are full of lifelike movement: the weird rock formations at the upper left seem half
alive; and overhead, a strangely shaped cloud, resembling
a comet or fireball, seems to follow the struggle below. The
abrupt transitions from light to dark, which are in good
part a product of the breadth, strength, and bluntness of
Dürer's etched line, cause the eye to move about the image
continuously without a point of focus or of rest. This rest-
less movement created by a flickering alternation of
strong lights and darks is similar to that found in the
Sudarium etching of the same year (cat. no. 193).

The curvilinear, calligraphic quality of the line in this
etching parallels the ornamental style of pen draughtsmanship which Dürer employed when designing the woodcuts
commissioned by Emperor Maximilian; compare the
unicorn of this etching with the horses of the *Triumphal
Chariot* (cat. no. 205).

Although not as evenly printed as it can be, this early
impression is a fine, clear one with only the very faintest
beginnings of rust spots on the brow of the girl and on the
rocks at the upper left. The sheet has been clipped along
the plate mark.

The subject has been variously interpreted: as the
abduction of Proserpine, daughter of Ceres, by Pluto, god
of the underworld; as a wild man out of the folk traditions
of medieval Europe; and as the Devil carrying off a witch.
All of these interpretations acknowledge the demonic,
infernal nature of the image. Dürer has, however, added
psychological complexity to the subject by representing
the abductor, who turns toward us rather than his prize,
with his features contracted not by lust or fury but by
pain or sorrow.

195

Meder 67, with rust marks, a
No visible watermark
Colls.: Robert-Dumesnil (Lugt 2200), H. F. Sewall (Lugt
1309)
Harvey D. Parker Collection   P336

At first glance this impression may seem superior to the
first owing to the dramatic effect produced by a whiter
paper and a selective inking and wiping of the plate which
reinforces the modeling. It should be noted that early
impressions of this etching are not usually characterized
by such selective inking and wiping.

Close examination reveals evidence of advanced corrosion of the plate; for example, the mottled white areas on
the rocks at the upper left and on the gravelly patch of
earth under the unicorn. The granular patch of rust on the
girl's brow is now more visible. The film of ink left on the
plate admittedly makes it difficult to determine the condition of the plate. It is quite possible that this film was
used to conceal the plate's true condition and, thereby, to
produce a more attractive impression. Although the impression lacks a watermark, the corrosion of the plate
classifies it as a posthumous printing according to Meder's
catalogue.

There are signs of carelessness in the inking and printing of the plate. Along the edges of the design many lines
lack ink and print as white rather than black lines. In
wiping the unworked areas of the plate to produce highlights, the printer has all too frequently dragged ink from
adjoining lines, causing conspicuous gray streaks across
white areas, as on the cloud with the monogram and date.
The sheet has been trimmed inside the plate mark following the borderline.

194. The Abduction (reduced)

195. The Abduction (reduced)

196. The Abduction (copy, reduced)

196

HIERONYMUS HOPFER
Germany, active circa 1528–1550
Copy after Dürer, B. 72
Etching, B. 42, 285 x 215 mm.
Coll.: H. F. Sewall (Lugt 1309)
Harvey D. Parker Collection   P2117

An etched copy by Hieronymus Hopfer, who worked both
in Nuremberg and in Augsburg, points up the special
qualities of Dürer's etched line. The image is reversed and
somewhat reduced. The presence of rust marks makes it
likely that the copy was also executed on an iron or steel
plate. The lines are conspicuously thinner than those of the
original. When one compares Dürer's etchings, such as
the *Agony in the Garden* (cat. no. 191), the *Abduction* (cat.
no. 194), or the *Landscape with the Cannon* (cat. no. 198),
with other German etchings of the first half of the sixteenth century, one sees that the breadth of his etched line
was quite exceptional. Hopfer, like most German etchers of
the time, sought a fineness in the etched line that is comparable to the lines of contemporary engravings. Dürer, on
the contrary, consciously exploited the breadth and
strength of line that the etching medium could produce.

Hopfer's copy also serves to make one even more conscious of the tremendous linear energy of Dürer's original
design. Hopfer's fine lines etched close together often read
as a continuous gray tone rather than as a bold calligraphic
pattern. The lines of the copy are more regular and, consequently, more static, as in the shading lines of the sky.

The paper is somewhat disfigured by yellow stains.

197. The Virgin on the Crescent with a Crown of Stars and a Scepter.

197

The Virgin on the Crescent with a Crown of Stars and a Scepter
Dated 1516
Engraving, 118 x 74 mm.
B. 32

Meder 37a
No visible watermark
Horatio Greenough Curtis Fund   51.728

This engraving reflects the technical achievements of the three great engravings, *Knight, Death, and the Devil; Saint Jerome in his Study;* and *Melencolia* (cat. nos. 179, 186, 188) in its mastery of the simultaneously descriptive and ornamental. The treatment of the folds of the Virgin's sleeve is very comparable to that of the skirt and purse of the woman in *Melencolia.* The effect of bursting light parallels the dramatic lighting of etchings such as the *Agony in the Garden* (cat. no. 191).

This particular impression, a fine, strong, and well-printed one, was selected for reproduction in Hollstein (no. 37). A recent examination under the microscope, however, revealed that numerous areas of the print have been skillfully retouched, making an excellent impression seem even finer. The retouching, which was probably done with a brush, is extremely difficult to discern with the unaided eye; under magnification the ink used can be distinguished as glossier, blacker, and slightly cooler in color than the ink of the printed lines themselves. The most obvious and extensive retouching is found in the plate mark (see detail) and in the aureoles around the figures, where lines parallel to, or superimposed on, the printed lines have been added. Several of the main contours of the drapery and figures have been reinforced by retouching (along the Virgin's right shoulder, for example), so have a few curls in her hair, the outline of her scepter, the monogram, the date, and a few shadow areas in the drapery (see detail).

The retouching has, with one or two minor exceptions in which weak or missing lines have been strengthened or replaced, been done in order to make an already fine impression appear more richly inked. Such retouching could only have been done to enhance the appeal of the print in a connoisseur's market.

197a. The Virgin on the Crescent with a Crown of Stars and a Scepter (enlarged detail of retouching with brush)

197b. The Virgin on the Crescent with a Crown of Stars and a Scepter (enlarged detail of Virgin's sleeve retouched with brush)

240

198. The Landscape with the Cannon

198

The Landscape with the Cannon
Dated 1518
Etching, 220 x 327 mm.
B. 99

Meder 96, before rust marks, a
Watermark: High crown (M. 31)
Colls.: Friedrich August II (Lugt 971), Tomás Harris
Katherine Eliot Bullard Fund   68.209

This, Dürer's last etching, is one of the earliest etchings by
any artist in which landscape is the principal subject. It is
appropriately panoramic in format, and, because it is conceived without a central point of focus, one is encouraged
to explore the landscape, which is partly based on Dürer's
silverpoint drawing of Kirchehrenbach near Forchheim
(W. 479). The costume worn by the foremost figure in the
group at the right derives from an early pen and watercolor
drawing of three Turks (W. 78) that he copied in Venice
from a painting by Gentile Bellini. The Turk's features are
those of Dürer himself as portrayed about this time in a
portrait medallion carved by Hans Schwarz.

The relationship of black printed line to the white paper
is strikingly different from that seen in Dürer's engravings
in these years. In the *Saint Anthony* of 1519 (cat. no. 210),
the delicate engraved lines blend optically with the white
of the paper to produce areas of finely graded gray tone.
The bolder lines of the etching, however, remain distinctly
separate and have their own ornamental value.

The impression, though fine, is not as evenly printed as
it can be. Part of Friedrich August's collector's stamp is
visible in the lower right corner.

199–200

The Crucifixion (Roundel)
About 1518
Engraving, diameter 40 mm.
B. 23

199

Meder 24 I, before reworking
No visible watermark
Harriet Otis Cruft Fund   22.1063

It seems likely that this tiny and very rare engraving was
not conceived of as a print by Dürer. The inscription above
Christ's head appears in reverse, but far more convincing
evidence is a letter written in 1520 to the secretary of Duke
Friedrich of Saxony in which Dürer says that he encloses
"two little prints of the Cross from a plate engraved in
gold" (Conway, p. 90). Such a gold plate was probably
intended as a hat decoration, like the disk of the Virgin
and Child worn by the Emperor Maximilian in Dürer's
woodcut (B. 154) and the similar one in Lucas van Leyden's
print (B. 172). As Dürer was in the service of Maximilian
until early 1519, it is possible that the gold disk was intended for him. On the basis of the high quality of the very
few existing impressions, as well as Dürer's letter, it would
appear that Dürer printed a few impressions himself before the plate left his hands.

200

ANONYMOUS ENGRAVER
Probably sixteenth century
Copy after Dürer, B. 23
Meder 24, Copy A
Coll.: H. F. Sewall (Lugt 1309)
Harvey D. Parker Collection   P285

This is an extraordinarily good and deceptive copy. The
differences require close study. In Dürer's print, small
groups of parallel lines accurately define shapes and
simultaneously shade them so as to produce a three-
dimensional effect. In the copy, the lines do not have the
same confidence nor do they achieve the same sense of
volume in the figures. One has only to compare the faces of
the kneeling Magdalen in the two versions. Dürer's lucid,
expressive lines suggest both the roundness of her face
and its sober regard, whereas the copyist's lines make her
face appear as a flat and vapid oval.

199. The Crucifixion (Roundel)

199a. The Crucifixion (Roundel) (enlarged)

200. The Crucifixion (Roundel) (copy)

200a. The Crucifixion (Roundel) (copy, enlarged)

201
The Virgin Mary Roundel above a Rocky Landscape

Shortly before 1515
Woodcut, 95 mm. diameter, 149 mm. high
Not in Bartsch

Meder 209b
No visible watermark
Coll.: Tomás Harris
Centennial Gift of Landon T. Clay   68.197

This attractive and unusual woodcut, which lacks Dürer's monogram, was not always accepted as his work in the nineteenth century; Bartsch did not include it in his catalogue. However, most modern Dürer scholars acknowledge its authenticity on the basis of quality and of its stylistic similarity to the 1512 woodcut *Saint Jerome in a Cave* (cat. no 172). Both prints are a departure from Dürer's highly sophisticated tonal woodcut style of 1510–1511. Depth and volume are not explored but only implied by groups of parallel hatchings that are relatively unmodulated in tone. These groupings of lines, particularly of the rocky landscape in this print, form a very subtle, almost abstract, surface pattern. The style, with its diminished range of tonal contrasts and greater emphasis on patterning, is a prelude to what Panofsky calls Dürer's "decorative style" that he employed in his designs for Emperor Maximilian.

Panofsky believes that both parts of the composition were designed by Dürer but that the artist had not intended that they be combined on one block. The format, however, with its incomplete lower borderline, seems too novel for a cutter to have conceived on his own, and the fact that impressions were printed up to ten years after the block was executed suggests that the combination of the two parts was more than an accident or whim. According to Meder's description of breaks in the circular borderline, the impression on exhibition was printed shortly after 1520. (The Museum of Fine Arts owns an impression of the *Roundel* alone, printed earlier than this one.) It is, however, exceptionally rare to find complete impressions today. Meder records six, but he had not seen this one. Early collectors seem to have frequently cut off the landscape and discarded it, perhaps because they found the unconventionality of the design disturbing.

201. The Virgin Mary Roundel above a Rocky Landscape

202–203
Rhinoceros
Dated 1515
Woodcut
B. 136

202
Meder 273, I
235 x 296 mm. (including inscription)
No visible watermark
Colls.: British Museum, duplicate (Lugt 302 and 305),
Tomás Harris
Stephen Bullard Memorial Fund   68.247

Dürer's fascination with the exotic and bizarre, of which
the engraving of the *Monstrous Sow of Landser* (cat. no. 8) is
an example, almost certainly prompted this woodcut.
Knowing his passionate interest in accurately rendering
natural phenomena, it is obvious that Dürer was not
working from nature when he portrayed this armored and
scaly creature labeled *Rhinocerus* and dated 1515. Documentary evidence proves that the rhinoceros in question
had been sent to the King of Portugal by an Indian sultan
in that year. Valentin Ferdinand, a Moravian painter living
in Portugal, sent an account and a sketch of the animal to a
friend of Dürer's. The inscription above the image is
Dürer's interpretation of these facts:

In the year 1513 [sic] A.D., on May 1, there was brought to
Emanuel of Lisbon, the great powerful king of Portugal,
such a living animal from India. They call it a rhinoceros.
It is represented here in its complete form. It has the color
of a speckled turtle. And it is almost entirely covered by a
thick shell [*von dicken Schalen uberlegt*]. And in size it is
like the elephant but lower on its legs, and almost invulnerable. It has a sharp strong horn on its nose, which it
starts to sharpen whenever it is near stones. The stupid
animal is the mortal enemy of the elephant. The elephant
fears it terribly, because where they encounter, it runs with
its head down between its front legs and fatally rips open
the stomach of the elephant which is unable to protect
itself. Because the animal is so well armed, the elephant
cannot do anything to it. They also say that the rhinoceros
is fast, lively and clever (translation from *Dürer in America*,
no. 200).

The reptilian appearance of the animal may be the result
of Dürer's misunderstanding of Ferdinand's description of
the animal's outer covering.

The woodcut was one of Dürer's most popular prints,
and Meder describes eight different printings in Germany
and the Netherlands. This impression is from the earliest
and only printing made during Dürer's life. Although the
paper is soiled, the impression is very fine.

203
Meder 273, VII, with chiaroscuro block
214 x 298 mm.
No visible watermark
Colls.: Earl of Aylesford (Lugt 58), Paul J. Sachs
Bequest of W. G. Russell Allen   1971.235

By the beginning of the seventeenth century, Dürer's block
for the *Rhinoceros* was in the Netherlands. About 1620,
Hendrik Hondius in the Hague printed it with a Dutch
translation of the inscription. Very shortly afterwards,
Willem Janssen of Amsterdam republished it as a chiaroscuro print by adding a block with a tone of color. His
edition seems to have lacked the inscription.

In the case of the *Rhinoceros* woodcut, the addition of the
tone block, here inked with a dark blue green, served many
functions. It enhanced the already decorative qualities of
the design by introducing an effect of light playing on the
beast's armor. It also gave added relief and bulk to its form.
Furthermore, and perhaps most important to Janssen, the
tone block successfully obscured the horizontal split and
broadened lines of Dürer's block.

Janssen added two tone blocks to Dürer's woodcut
portrait of *Ulrich Varnbüler* (cat. no. 207) with similarly
attractive results. It is probable that the addition of color to
what would otherwise be very tired impressions made
them more saleable.

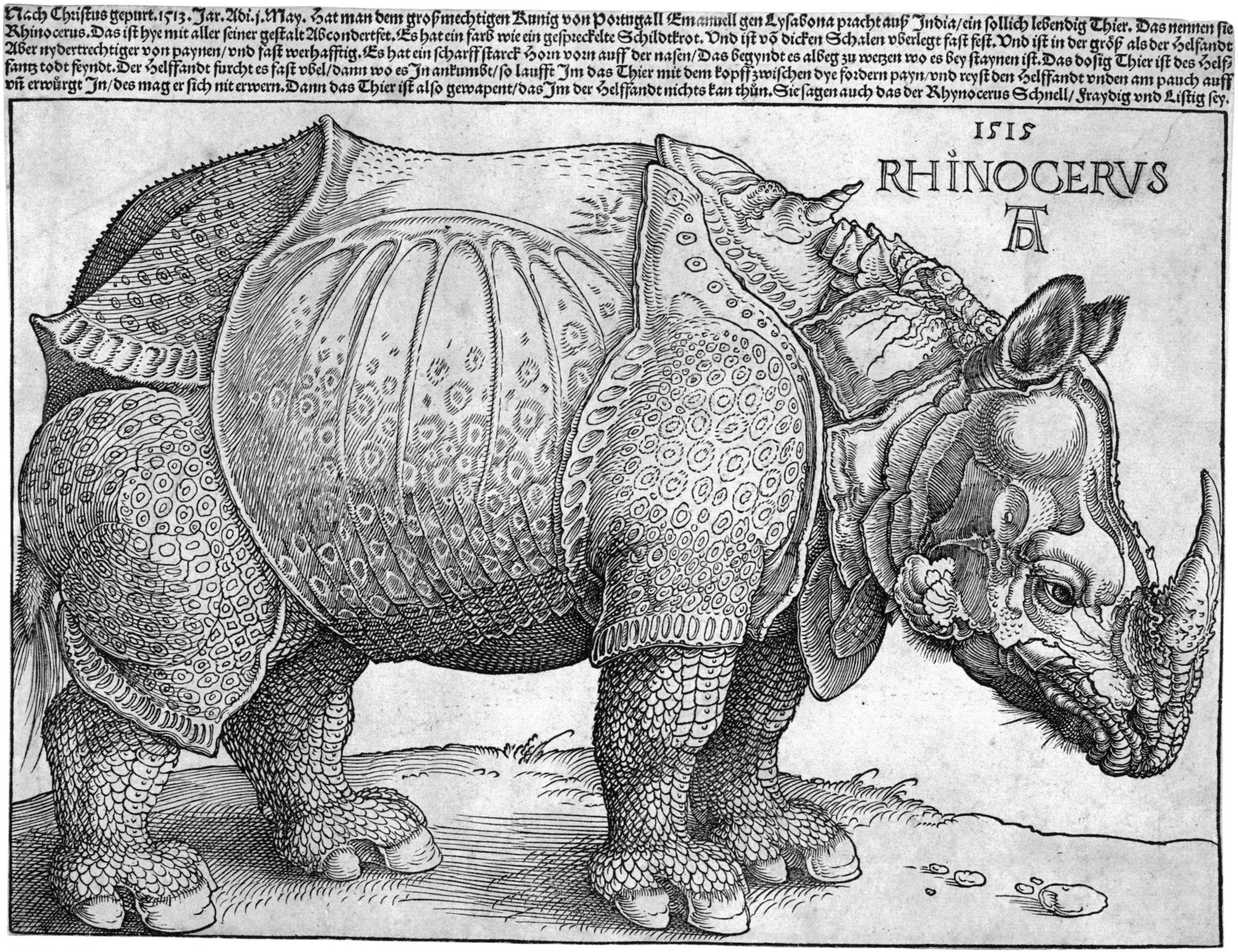

RHINOCERVS

ISIS

1513

Nach Christus gepurt.1513. Jar. Adi. j. May. hat man dem großmechtigen Kunig von Portugall Emanuell gen Lysabona pracht auß India/ein sollich lebendig Thier. Das nennen sie Rhinocerus. Das ist hye mit aller seiner gestalt Abconterfet. Es hat ein farb wie ein gespeckelte Schildtrot. Vnd ist von dicken Schalen vberlegt fast fest. Vnd ist in der größ als der Helfandt Aber nydertrechtiger von paynen/vnd fast werhafftig. Es hat ein scharff starck horn von an auff der nasen/Das begyndt es allweg zu wetzen wo es bey staynen ist. Das dosig Thier ist des Helfands todt feyndt. Der Helfandt furcht es fast vbel/dann wo es In ankumbt/so laufft Jm das Thier mit dem kopff zwischen dye fordern payn/vnd reyst den Helfandt vnden am pauch auff vñ erwürgt Jn/des mag er sich nit erweren. Dann das Thier ist also gewapent/das Jm der Helffandt nichts kan thun. Sie sagen auch das der Rhynocerus Schnell/Fraydig vnd Listig sey.

202. The Rhinoceros (reduced)

245

203. The Rhinoceros (chiaroscuro, reduced)

204

Triumphal Arch of Maximilian I
Dated 1515 (cut 1515–1517)
Woodcut, 3409 x 2922 mm.
B. 138

Meder 251, first edition
Watermark: Imperial eagle (M. 238)
Colls.: Nicholas Meldemann; F. Ulrich, Prince Kinsky,
Vienna
Otis Norcross Fund   51.415

In 1512, Emperor Maximilian I commissioned Dürer to participate in a program of artistic projects to glorify and immortalize his person, the Hapsburg House of Austria, and the Holy Roman Empire. The Emperor was a generous and impulsive man, able and complex in character; one of the last kings who tried to be a great knight—he dreamed of leading a crusade against the infidels. Maximilian also attempted to fulfill an ideal of his own day, to be a man who had had some knowledge of every field, whether statecraft, cooking, mining, fashion designing, music, printing, classical archaeology, or, most of all, mechanized warfare. Maximilian turned principally to printed images and texts to make his achievements and ideas known throughout the world because he recognized the great efficacy of printed matter.

The printed projects on which Dürer collaborated were the *Triumphal Arch, Triumphal Procession,* Maximilian's *Prayerbook,* and *Freydal,* a history of the emperor's tournaments and masquerades. The *Triumphal Arch,* for which Dürer was the designer-in-chief, was the only project to be completed before Maximilian's death in 1519. Grandiose in scale, the arch consisted of one hundred and ninety-two woodblocks printed on thirty-six sheets of paper which, when assembled, measure eleven feet, eight and one half inches in height, by nine feet, eight inches in width. Maximilian himself proposed the Roman arch form and the subjects of its embellishment. Johannes Stabius, his court astronomer and historian, supervised the program, including particulars about the emperor's actual and spiritual ancestors; his political, military, and personal accomplishments; the heraldry of his far-flung imperial territories; portraits of past and contemporary rulers, popes and saints; and, finally, ornaments of allegorical significance. Five sheets of text with Stabius' description of the program and explanation of the allegories were printed to accompany the arch. Jorg Kölderer, whose coat-of-arms rests between Stabius' and Dürer's on the lowest of the right central steps, executed the architectural design, which

bears little resemblance to its antique prototypes. It is probable that the final, curious form of the woodcut arch was the result of the ever-increasing amounts of information it was required to carry.

Although Dürer probably supervised and approved the drawings for the arch, a relatively small proportion of it seems to have been cut directly from his designs. The other artists who made drawings for the arch were Hans Springinklee, Wolf Traut, Albrecht Altdorfer, and Dürer's brother Hans. Willibald Pirckheimer, a noted humanist and classical scholar and Dürer's close friend, advised him on the allegorical ornament. In a letter of 1515, Dürer requested payment and claimed credit for having completed most of the ornamental work. By then, all the designs seem to have been completed, since the last historical episode depicted is the 1515 Congress of Princes at Vienna; and the arch was given that date in both lower corners. However, the blocks had not yet been cut, and the task was entrusted to the Nuremberg workshop of Hieronymus Andreä (or Resch). The cutting and printing, interrupted by disputes about iconography and genealogy, was not completed until early in 1518.

There are five editions of the *Triumphal Arch.* The first edition of 1517–1518 is characterized by corrections of iconography and genealogy in the form of slips of paper printed with the corrections and pasted over the original inscriptions. The set owned by the Museum of Fine Arts, of which four sheets are exhibited, is particularly interesting. It once belonged to Nicholas Meldemann, a sixteenth-century Nuremberg painter, publisher, and woodblock cutter, whose signature, notations, and collation marks appear on the versos of the sheets. Henry P. Rossiter (see *MFA Bulletin,* vol. XLIX, 1951, pp. 95–98) suggests that Meldemann helped Hieronymus Andreä with the cutting and printing of the blocks. In 1526, Archduke Ferdinand ordered the blocks to be reprinted in Vienna. Very few examples of this second edition have survived, but three further editions were printed in Vienna in 1559, 1799, and 1885–1886.

The fourth edition, 1799, was published by Adam Bartsch, the great print cataloguer and amateur printmaker, who made etched copies to replace several missing blocks. The surviving blocks are preserved in the Albertina, Vienna.

The small blocks with historical scenes were published separately at least four times, and impressions are found without the surrounding ornament.

The following four sheets from the first edition have been selected to illustrate the nature of Dürer's contribution to the *Triumphal Arch.*

A

The Central Cupola with Tabernacle of the Mystery of Egyptian Hieroglyphs

Only the tabernacle of the cupola is thought to be after a drawing by Dürer. Pirckheimer was largely responsible for the iconography of the portrayal of Maximilian. He had translated into Latin the second- or fourth-century Greek manuscript of Horus Apollo's Egyptian *Hieroglyphica*. The manuscript contained visual symbols, or "emblems," representing qualities or ideal attributes, and it fascinated classical scholars and humanists. With the use of the *Hieroglyphica*, a message extolling Maximilian can be decoded in Dürer's tabernacle design. (For the translation, see Panofsky, vol. I, p. 177.)

B

Upper Section of the Central Portal of Honor and Might

This entire sheet, printed from one large block with an insert of the winged woman, is considered to be entirely designed by Dürer. It is typical of the inventiveness of the decoration covering the whole arch. Sculptured architectural adornments, such as vines, laurel wreaths, and pomegranates, are combined with "living" cranes, griffons, soldiers, and lilies of the valley, all of which have allegorical significance.

As may be observed here, the entire arch is unified in terms of a single light source coming from the right.

C

Tablet at Upper Right with Inscription on Goat's Skin above Twelve Busts of Royal Persons, with Drummers and Griffon

The twelve royal persons, and possibly the tablet, are the designs of another artist, but Dürer is thought to be responsible for the rest. A comparison of the goats, dogs, and putti on either side of the tablet suggests Dürer's working method. The group on the left is more graceful and convincing than the same group that appears in reverse on the right. Dürer's practice seems to have been to provide a drawing for a motif that could be cut for one side and reversed by an assistant to be used on the other.

D

Six Historical Panels and Portion of Right Inner Column

Ascribed to Dürer are the column and the two historical compartments in the bottom row. The first represents Maximilian meeting Henry VIII of England at the Battle of Spurs and the second, Maximilian, Ladislaus of Hungary, and Sigismund of Poland with Maximilian's granddaughter, Mary, and Ladislaus' children, Louis and Ann.

On the column is a chain composed of goat's head, flowering urns, a medal with the Virgin and Child and heraldic griffon; it is the insignia of the Order of Temperance to which Maximilian belonged.

204. Triumphal Arch of Maximilian I (reduced)

250

204A. Triumphal Arch of Maximilian I: Central Cupola with Tabernacle of the Mystery of Egyptian Hieroglyphs (reduced detail)

204B. Triumphal Arch of Maximilian I: Upper Section of Central Portal of Honor and Might (reduced detail)

251

252

204C. Triumphal Arch of Maximilian I: Tablet at Upper Right with Inscription on Goat's Skin above Twelve Busts of Royal Persons, with Drummers and Griffon (reduced detail)

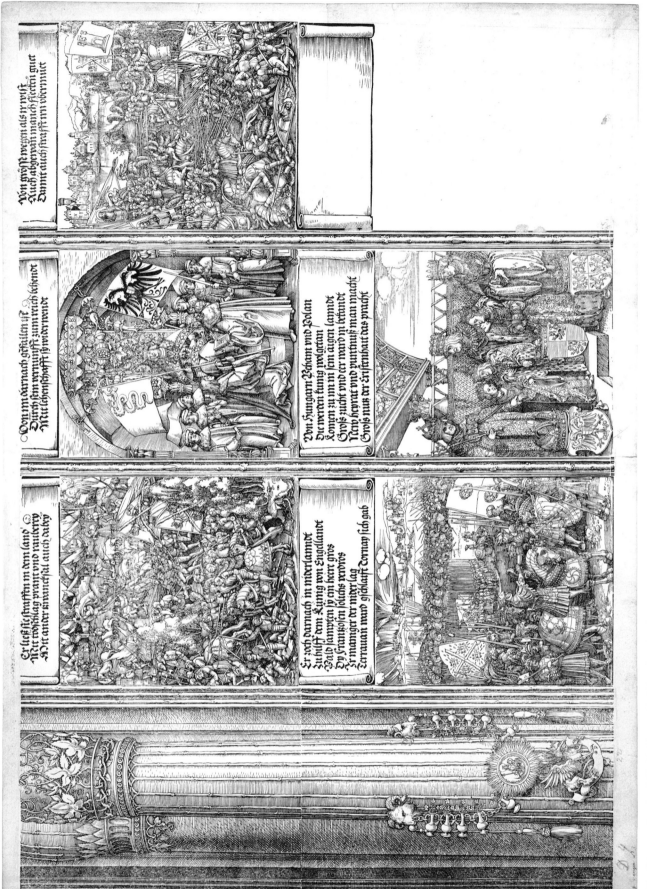

204D. Triumphal Arch of Maximilian I: Six Historical Panels and Portion of Right Inner Column (reduced detail)

205. Triumphal Chariot of Maximilian I (reduced)

Diser nachuerzeychenter Eren oder Triumph wagen ist den allerdurchleuchtigisten Großmechtigisten herrn weyland Keyser Maximilian hochlöblicher gedechtnuß unserm aller gnedigisten herrn zu sondern eren erfunden unnd verordent, unnd zu unnterthenigem gefallen dem großmechtigisten yetz Regieren den Keyser Karolo rc. durch Albrecht Dürer daselbst in das werck gemacht.

Erstlich dieweyl Kayserlich May, alle Künig unnd herren mit glori magnificent, rc, unnd wirdigkeyt übertrifft, so ist der selb wagen auff vier eren reder, darauff ihr Keyserlich May, solcher überrechligkeyt halben billich empor gefürt werden soll gestelt. Nemlich als Gloriam, Magnificentiam, Dignitatem unnd Honorem.

Nachuolgent seind an den vier eren rädern des wagens die vier angehengt an stat vier reder gesetzt, Nemlich Iustitia Fortitudo, Prudentia, Temperantia. Auff welchen all ander tugent ein anfang unnd ursprung haben, an die auch kein Künig oder herr volkumen seyn kan oder mag. Dann wo die Gerechtigkeyt, Mannlich sterck, des gemüts, die Vernunfft unnd Beschedenheyt mangelt, kan kein Reych bestendig seyn.

Nach dem Moderatio unnd Prouidentia der vernunfft am nechsten sind füren die selben zwo tugent die zwey nechsten pferd, die der vernunfft, damit der wag mit rechter maß unnd fürsichtigkeyt seinen gang haben mag.

Dieweyl auch dise vier tugend aneynander hangen, unnd von einander nit gesondert werden mögen also, wo eine der selben mangelt das die ander nit volkumen seyn kan. So sind die selben vier mit den andern ihro anhangenden tugenden so auff neu füssen zusamen gefügt, unnd ineinander verschlossen. Nemlich dieweyl Iustitia gehört, und haben müß Veritatem, so helt sie in der lincken hand ein krantz der Warheyt. In den auch die Messigkeyt mit der rechten hand greufft, daß wo die Warheyt nit ist, kan die Gerechtigkeyt nit statt haben. Die Messigkeyt mag auch so sie von der Warheyt weycht, nit mer Messigkeyt genant werden.

Mit der rechten hand greufft Iustitia in den krantz Clementie das langt an, daß die Gerechtigkeyt nit gantz zu streng sonder mit Mildigkeyt soll vermischt seyn. In disen krantz zu gehören der mitter frantz Equitatis, dann so wol als die Gerechtigkeyt nit zu scharpff seyn, also soll sie auch nit alle maß, und in allen sachen zu uil und oder barmhertzig sonder Equa unnd gleych seyn, an welche Gleychheyt die Gerechtigkeyt nit bessern mag.

Die nachuolgende zwey pferd werden durch Alacritatem und Opportunitatem gefürt. Darumb als wol sichs gezimpt daß zu bequemer zeyt der wagen für sich gerüst sich auch das solchs frölich unnd mit einer freyheyt beschehe.

PROVIDENTIA · ALACRITAS · MODERATIO · OPORTVNITAS

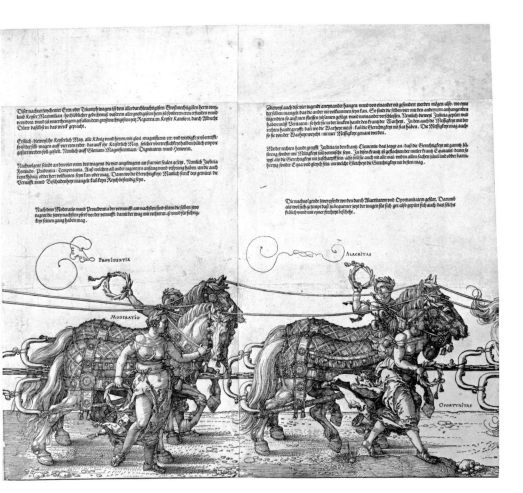

Und damit diser wagen recht unnd wol gefürt werd ist Ratio zuuorderst an, für einen fürman unnd weglanter gesetzt, darumb das alle beseitige ding mit vernunfft geschehen sollen. Die selbig Ratio helt auch zwayen zusammen eyn Nobilitatis das ander Potentie, angesehen daß die Kayser. May, alle Künig unnd herrn mit adel unnd macht übertroffen hat.

Und auff daß die pferd so an den wagen gespant sind, mit als unuernünfftige thier auch dem weg der Verstendigkeyt lauffen sonder deser statlichen durch Vernunfft regiert werden mögen so hat ein yetlich pferd seine lanter un halter damit es nit anders gern noch lauffen möge, daß wie sich nach eygenschafft der selben tugend gehört.

Und dieweil alle menschen nach dem willen gottes regiert werden, nechd daß sagen die weysen daß in so uberderst das hertz des Künigs in der hande gotes stee, der das uund nach seinem göttlichen wolgefallen wendet unnd khert, darumb so becket wo der Keyserlichen May, diß geschrift. In manu dei rc Regis est. Und für das wort Cor ist zu mercken seitig stee ein herr mit einer Laurea gemalet. Bedeutet das edel hertz Keyserlicher May, so mit allen tugenden unnd eren gezieret unnd geziert gewesst ist.

Darnach gern zwey pferd die stetigs für sich begeren, werden durch Magnanimitatem unnd Audatiam regiert.

Dieweyl auch mit warheyt gesagt werden mag, daß weyland die Kayserliche May, mit irer tierd un Klarheyt auff erden, als den das das die schönist Sun am himel geweest ist, so wirt ob irer May, dise schrifft gesetzt. Quod in celis Sol, hoc in terra Cesar. Und ist für das wort Sol ein Sun gemalet, wie für das wort Cesar ain Adler.

Maximilian von Gottes gnaden
E. Römischer Kayser. rc

Ersamer lieber getreuer wir haben den Triumphwagen mitsampt der Exposition den du uns zu unterthenigem gefallen zu zier unsers Triumphs erdacht unnd gestelt. Auch durch Albrecht Dürer aufreissen lassen, unnd bey soger diß briefs zugesendt hast empfangen den auch notturfftiglich übersehen unn tragen an solchem deinem erfunden fleiß un erboten sonder gnädigs wolgefallen, sind geneygt das in sondern gnaden gegen dir zu erkennen wollten wir dir gnädiger meynung nit verhalten. Geben in unser Stat Instruck am Neunundzwentzigisten Martii Anno. rc. xviij. unsers Reychs am. xxij. jarrn.

Per Regem per se.

Ad Mandatum Cesaree Maiestatis propium,
Weisner.

Dem Ersamen unserm Rat / und der Reychs lieben getreuen Wilhalden Pirckhaymer.

Damit der du die großmütigkeyt unnd keckheyt den wagen nit verfären so seind für die selben zuuorderst zwen ander Roß gespant, die werden durch Experientiam und Solertiam gemaystert. Dan wo die erfarnuß un fürrechtigkeyt nit ist, mag die Keckheyt und Großmütigkeyt leycht schad bringen.

Diser wagen ist zu Nürmberg erfunden gerissen unnd gedruckt durch Albrechten Dürer / im jar. M. D. xxij.

Cum Gratia et Priuilegio Cesaree Maiestatis.

MAGNANIMITAS · AVDATIA · EXPERIENTIA · SOLERTIA

QVOD·IN·CELIS·SOL·   HOC·IN·TERRA·
                     CAESAR·EST·

CLEMENTIA   TEMPERANTIA

VERITAS   LIBERALITAS

AEQVITAS

IN·M ANV DE I   REG IS·E ST S

SECVRITAS

205a. Triumphal Chariot of Maximilian I (actual size detail)

205

Triumphal Chariot of Maximilian I
Dated 1522, begun 1518
Woodcut, 450 x 2281 mm.
B. 139

Meder 252, first edition
Watermark: Cross (M. 146)
Coll.: Dr. A. Sträter (Lugt 787)
Maria Antoinette Evans Fund   M32608

One of the woodcut projects on which Dürer worked for the Emperor Maximilian was the *Triumphal Procession,* which was intended to be some sixty yards long. Unfinished during Maximilian's lifetime, it was printed in an incomplete form in 1526. Even then, it did not include the emperor's chariot since Dürer had withdrawn his designs for it at Maximilian's death in 1519; in 1522, having revised the iconography and design, Dürer published it as the *Great Triumphal Car.* Willibald Pirckheimer had assisted in the revision and suggested the addition of a regalia of emblems and twenty-two women personifying the Virtues to the Emperor Maximilian in his grand chariot.

The *Triumphal Chariot,* the *Triumphal Arch* (cat. no. 204), and other woodcuts executed during the years 1512–1522 are described by Panofsky as being in the "decorative style." This style had begun to be evident in the 1512 *Saint Jerome in a Cave* (cat. no. 172) and emerged fully in the *Rhinoceros* (cat. no. 202) and in Dürer's work for Maximilian. The full-blown style — princely, ornate, and elegant and characterized by a rich, surface pattern — was adopted by Dürer as appropriate to the nature of the projects. The *Chariot,* printed on eight sheets of paper, has theatrical effects of light and color. The Virtues are dramatically modeled in tones of white, gray, and dark gray, without intermediate gradations. A strong light illuminates each section from the left and unifies the whole design. The skirts of the Virtues alongside the horses flutter in the wind, and each of the horses prances; but the degree of animation varies from block to block and is determined by the nature of the particular Virtues named. For instance, Skill and Experience, at the head of the procession, move at a slower pace than Speed and Strength, on the fifth sheet. The fine lines of the flourishes decorating the names of these Virtues curiously resemble puffs of clouds and further contribute to the sense of motion. In Dürer's later engravings and woodcuts, one sees a return to more natural and solidly modeled forms and rationally constructed compositions.

This complete impression of the *Triumphal Chariot of Maximilian* is from the first of seven editions recorded by Meder, which was the only printing supervised by Dürer. Each of the eight sheets was at one time cut close to the printed image, eliminating the identifying letters, A through H, that had been printed in the lower margins. A subsequent owner attached late seventeenth-century paper to the top left corner and at the top of the last seven sections to make the sheet sizes uniform again.

206

The Virgin as Queen of the Angels
Dated 1518
Woodcut, 301 x 214 mm.
B. 101

Meder 211a
Watermark: Bull's head with serpent (M. 69)
Stephen Bullard Memorial Fund   40.13

Executed in 1518, the same year that the *Triumphal Arch of Maximilian I* (cat. no. 204) finally appeared, the *Virgin as Queen of the Angels* possesses the same rich, ornate style and concern with detail, but on a far more intimate scale. Its smaller format made it more likely to be bought by a much wider public.

The surface of the composition sparkles with light and movement. A diffuse light pouring in from the right strikes the ornamental detail and highlights the Virgin, Child, and foreground angels, while their contours and the angels behind them seem to dissolve in shadow. A more intense brightness is cast by the halos of the Virgin and Child. While the linear quality of the print is subordinate to the effects of almost theatrical lighting, some of the lines, such as those of the drapery of the crowning angels, have great calligraphic beauty reminiscent of Dürer's early woodcuts (see *Samson,* cat. no. 24). The fineness of line, so apparent in an early impression such as this, contributes to an effect of incorporeal buoyancy.

207

Ulrich Varnbüler
Dated 1522
Woodcut, 487 x 326 mm.
B. 155

Meder 256, I, b
No visible watermark
Bequest of W. G. Russell Allen   1971.232

Woodcut was not a common medium for portraiture until the sixteenth century. Dürer, whose many portrait drawings were justly admired, did not turn to portraiture in his prints until 1518, when he produced a woodcut of Emperor Maximilian.

Ulrich Varnbüler was a high official in the Supreme Court of the Empire and also a good friend of Dürer's. The portrait of Varnbüler, in almost full profile, expands dynamically out of its borders. This impression is a fine, early one, vividly communicating the richness of contrasts and variety of lines that describe delicate embroidery and heavy fabric, as well as the hulking strength of the sitter. The inscription offers Dürer's testimonial to the sitter's accomplishments as a public official and talents as a scholar. The inscription is interrupted by a vertical white strip. Panofsky suggests that the missing letters may form an anagram of a variant of Varnbüler's name (vol. II, p. 45, no. 369).

Willem Janssen in Amsterdam acquired the woodblock, as he had the *Rhinoceros* block (cat. no. 203), and printed chiaroscuro impressions with two tone blocks which are remarkably attractive.

206. The Virgin as Queen of the Angels (reduced)

VLRICHVS VARNBVLER ZC.M,D,XXII.

207. Ulrich Varnbüler (reduced)

208–209

The Last Supper

Dated 1523
Woodcut, 213 x 300 mm.
B. 53

208

Meder 184a
Watermark: High crown (M. 20)
Maria Antoinette Evans Fund   M32601

From the evidence of a number of surviving drawings with horizontal format dating from 1520–1524, it seems that Dürer may have been working on a third woodcut Passion series. The *Last Supper* of 1523, derived from a drawing of the same year (W. 889), is the only completed woodcut.

By this time, Dürer had turned away from the more decorative style of the woodcuts executed for the Emperor Maximilian. In this print, his basic vocabulary of lines is not essentially different from his tonal woodcut style that had first become evident in 1510. When one compares this print with the *Last Supper* from the *Large Passion* (cat. no. 154) one sees that in 1523 Dürer's systems of lines have been further simplified, the surface planes made more ample, and the tonal values reduced to a very narrow range of grays. The economy and restraint of the image is also emphasized by the absence of any description of texture, of ornamental details, or of dramatic illumination; and the overall lighting is generalized and somewhat austere. Whereas in the earlier *Last Supper,* the brightness of Christ's halo established him as the center of focus, here the round window serves that purpose. The figures are compressed into the narrow space behind and beside the table, giving them an added sense of solidity and monumentality.

The impression is early and of the highest quality. The warm tone of the paper and relative paleness of the ink brings the subtly combined tonal values of the composition into closer unity. The sober, restrained effect is suited to the scene. Dürer did not depict the supper itself but, rather, a moment that has almost never been portrayed. The guilty Judas has left, and Christ binds the remaining apostles in their love for one another as his disciples. (See Panofsky, vol. I, pp. 222–223 for a discussion of the relationship of this print to Protestantism.)

209

Meder 184e
No visible watermark
Coll.: Tomás Harris
Bequest of Francis Bullard, by sale of duplicates   68.278

A cursory glance at this impression of the *Last Supper* makes it appear to be of higher quality than cat. no. 208. The whiter paper provides a stronger contrast with the ink, creating an effect of brilliance. There were however wormholes and two horizontal splits in the block when this impression was printed. One split can be seen running from the left border through the tablecloth as far as the chalice; the other begins at the right borderline and runs through the edge of the tablecloth, almost to the center of the table leg. The latter split is slightly visible in the earlier impression, although Meder did not record it as characteristic of this earliest group. Both splits probably resulted from a join in the block that had widened. According to Meder's description of the block's condition, this impression was probably printed about 1600.

A careful comparison of this impression with the very early impression reveals that, even with Dürer's simplified woodcut style, in which the design is conceived in terms of tone rather than lines, there is still a visible depreciation when the lines of the block wear. As noted in the later impression of the *Mass of Saint Gregory* (cat. no. 168), the broadening of the contour lines of figures causes a flattening of forms and volume. Because the print is characterized by such harmony and economy, the broader, darker cross-hatched lines are distracting; folds of drapery, particularly, have assumed too much importance.

208. The Last Supper (reduced)

209. The Last Supper (reduced)

263

210. Saint Anthony

210

Saint Anthony

Dated 1519
Engraving, 100 x 143 mm.
B. 58

Meder 51a
No visible watermark
Colls.: G. Archinto (Lugt 52), H. von Bayer (Lugt 1293)
Gift of William Norton Bullard   M29851

From 1519 on Dürer continued to reduce even further the
contrasts and tonal range of his engravings. They are
lightly worked throughout and have a clear silvery aspect
that is totally new and, in early impressions, extremely
expressive. Light still plays an important role in very fine
impressions, but the effect is muted to conform to the
limited scale of grays. Highlights are kept to a minimum
and tend to be visible only on primary figures.

In this fine impression, cut on the plate mark, false
margins have been added on all four sides. This is readily
seen in the difference in paper color and in the rippling
of the marginal strips. The plate mark has been drawn in
with pen, and a few lines have been added at the lower
edge of the image in an attempt to improve the print by
straightening its original wavy border line.

211

A Peasant and His Wife

Dated 1519
Engraving, 117 x 74 mm.
B. 89

Meder 89b
No visible watermark
Colls.: P. Mariette (Lugt 1788), H. F. Sewall (Lugt 1309)
Harvey D. Parker Collection   P354

In this engraving, as in others of 1518–1526, the lightly
engraved lines of shading set close together produce the
effect of a gray tone.

A comparison of this print with *The Cook and His Wife*
(cat. no. 10), engraved some twenty years earlier, is
enlightening because it shows how different both Dürer's
pictorial style and method of engraving were in these two
periods. In the early engraving, the couple is standing
before a blank background and is depicted in terms of
contours, a manner very similar to Schongauer's. The 1519

211. A Peasant and His Wife

peasants, standing before a darkened stone wall, combine
a sculptural monumentality with solid realism and
individual characterization. In the early print, Dürer
employed sharp contrasts of black and white; the later
print is composed of a range of grays. The earlier engraved
lines swell and taper, providing a decorative interest in
themselves; the later lines are of uniform width and
resemble finely etched lines. In *The Cook and His Wife*
Dürer used contour lines to define form, and they are the
primary component of the figures. In *A Peasant and
His Wife*, he used tonal contrasts to define form. His
earlier use of decorative, expressive contour lines has
changed, and now he lets the subtleties of interior
modeling create decorative interest.

The impression is a very good one. Small spots of
corrosion are visible on the eggs and on the man's smock
above his right knee. These spots appear even on the very
earliest impressions. Mariette's signature, penned on the
verso, bled through onto the rock with Dürer's monogram.

212. Madonna with the Swaddled Infant

212
Madonna with the Swaddled Infant
Dated 1520
Engraving, 142 x 95 mm.
B. 38

Meder 40b
No visible watermark
Coll.: H. F. Sewall (Lugt 1309)
Harvey D. Parker Collection   P303

Compared to the *Virgin and Child Seated by a Wall* of 1514 (cat. no. 185) this print appears much less complex. Contributing to this simplicity are the regularized shapes of the figures. The Madonna's skirt is described with the geometric severity of the polyhedron in *Melencolia* (cat. no. 188). It is night; almost the whole of the plate has been darkened by shading with fine parallel lines, cross-hatching, flicks, or other patterns. The unworked areas depict light: the radiance of the haloes and a light from the left that illuminates the figures. Every detail, such as ruffled sleeves or pillow tassels, is veiled in shadow and subordinated entirely to the main theme. In this fine impression, the landscape background has been further shaded by ink left on the surface of the plate before printing. This tone is particularly visible on the hills behind the town at the left. In its simplicity, severity, and sense of volume, this is surely the most monumental of Dürer's Madonnas.

The solemn gaze of the Virgin, who looks down at the sleeping infant, combined with the darkness and the somber mood of the scene, suggest a prefiguration of the death of Christ.

213. Saint Christopher

213
Saint Christopher
Dated 1521
Engraving, 117 x 76 mm.
B. 51

Meder 53a
No visible watermark
Colls.: R. Balmanno (Lugt 213), H. F. Sewall (Lugt 1309)
Harvey D. Parker Collection   P316

As in the *Madonna with the Swaddled Infant* (cat. no. 212),
there are two sources of light in this print: the moon and
the child's halo. The rest of the plate is almost entirely
shaded with lightly engraved lines of hatching. In this
fine impression, the tonal effect of the lines is further
emphasized by a film of ink that was left on much of the
plate. Although this film is difficult to see, it may be
discerned on the flame of the monk's torch in the right
background and on the saint's staff below his hands. The
highlights of the staff are wiped clean on the upper
portion, where it is brightly lit by the radiance from the
Christ Child. Such use of plate tone is extremely subtle;
it reinforces the pattern of dramatic illumination, the
sculptural qualities of the figures, and the mood. In
this case, there is a sense of enlightenment, for Christ
has just revealed his identity to Christopher.

214

Saint Philip

Engraved 1523; redated and issued 1526
Engraving, 122 x 74 mm.
B. 46

Meder 48a
No visible watermark
Colls.: J. Malcolm (Lugt 1780), British Museum duplicate
(Lugt 305), Tomás Harris
Centennial Gift of Landon T. Clay   68.192

In this print the columnar folds of Saint Philip's unadorned cloak were Dürer's primary concern, and it is the
emphasis on the weight and volume of the cloak that
gives the figure an appearance of monumental sculpture.
The simplicity and naturalism of the background increase
the feeling of his solidity. These three-dimensional
qualities are achieved by the disciplined, subtle tonal
effects of hatching, characteristic of Dürer's late engravings, which can be readily seen in this fine impression.

The date on the tablet was changed from 1523 to 1526.
In the large painting of the *Four Apostles* presented to the
city of Nuremberg in 1526, Dürer used the same figure
study for Saint Paul. The only convincing reason that has
been suggested for the change of date on the print, is that
Dürer may have withheld the print until after the presentation of the painting to increase sales of the print.

214. Saint Philip

215–216
Cardinal Albrecht of Brandenburg
Dated 1523
Engraving, 176 x 130 mm.
B. 103

215
Meder 101, I, b
Watermark: Little jug with DB (M. 159)
Coll.: B. Hausmann (Lugt 377)
Maria Antoinette Evans Fund   M32599

Lightly hatched in a variety of gray tones, as most of
Dürer's late engravings, the quality of impression of this
plate should be judged by the standards of sculpture.
In fine early impressions, such as this one, the planes
of his face are modeled as a relief portrait medallion.

The portrait is based on Dürer's silverpoint drawing
(W. 896) that has a comparably delicate tonal quality.
In 1523, Dürer wrote to the Cardinal to say that he was
sending him the copper plate together with five hundred
impressions. The large number of impressions can be
explained by their probable intended use as bookplates.
The *Melanchthon* (cat. no. 217) and three of the four
remaining portraits in this medium may have been
engraved by Dürer for the same purpose.

This impression was printed with considerable care,
the coat-of-arms being wiped cleaner than the surrounding background, which has a thin film of ink left on it.

216
Meder 101, II
Watermark: Large city gate (M. 263)
Coll.: H. F. Sewall (Lugt 1309)
Harvey D. Parker Collection   P369

As one can tell from the loss of modeling in the face and
the broken, uneven lines throughout, the plate had worn
badly by the time this impression was taken. The plate
has also been reworked, probably in the mid-sixteenth
century, according to Meder's date of after 1550 for the
watermark. The major contours have been redrawn, and
the trial outline of the Cardinal's chest, which Dürer had
corrected and blended into the background, has been
misunderstood as a shadow and strengthened.

217
Philip Melanchthon
Dated 1526
Engraving, 175 x 128 mm.
B. 105

Meder 104a
No visible watermark.
Colls.: V. Mayer (Lugt 2525), Tomás Harris
Stephen Bullard Memorial Fund   68.238

The ascetic looking Melanchthon was a German educator
and Protestant theologian. A sense of otherworldliness is
suggested by the background of sky and the faraway gaze
in his eye. This ethereal mood is reinforced by the subtle
tonal qualities of the lightly engraved lines. A window is
reflected in Melanchthon's eye. This device is not unusual;
Dürer used it in four of his six engraved portraits, and it
has sometimes been taken as a reference to the eyes as
"windows of the soul." Melanchthon is simply dressed
and bareheaded, and more is revealed of the inner man
than of the outer in spite of the modest inscription:
"Dürer was able to depict Philip's features as if living,
but the practiced hand could not portray his soul"
(translation from *Dürer in America*, pp. 157–158).

The printed lines are in quite good condition, despite
evidence that the sheet was once folded several times.
A carefully repaired tear, scarcely visible to the naked eye,
extends from the upper margin down through
Melanchthon's temple to the left corner of his eye.
The plate mark and the shading under the tablet with
the inscription appear to have been strengthened at
certain points with brush and ink.

215. Cardinal Albrecht of Brandenburg

MDXXIII
SIC·OCVLOS·SIC·ILLE·GENAS·SIC·ORA·FEREBAT·
ANNO·ETATIS·SVE·XXXIIII

ALBERTVS·MI·DI·SA·SANC·ROMANAE·ECCLAE·TI·SAN·
CHRYSOGONI·PBR·CARDINA·MAGVN·AC·MAGDE·
ARCHIEPS·ELECTOR·IMPE·PRIMAS·ADMINI·
HALBER·MARCHI·BRANDENBVRGENSIS·

216. Cardinal Albrecht of Brandenburg

217. Philip Melanchthon

218–221
ILLUSTRATED BOOKS

The books exhibited were written and illustrated by Dürer. They contain three fragments of a comprehensive work on the theory and practice of art. The bulk of it remained in manuscript form: outlines; random notes; texts written, amended, and recopied; drawings and sketches. The writing had certainly been begun by 1512. From the manuscripts owned by the British Museum and the Dresden Landesbibliothek, it is evident that Dürer intended to write about the inborn gifts and education of an artist and about proportion, perspective, light and shadow, color, painting, architecture, geometry, and even music and fencing. In short, he wished to formulate a great code of laws governing art, geometry, education, and science to benefit future generations of artists. The unwieldy scope of his endeavor was gradually reduced. One section, the *Underweysung der Messung,* on the art of measurement, was published by Dürer himself in 1525; a second, *Befestigung,* on fortification, in 1527. A third, *Vier Bücher von Menschlicher Proportion*, on human proportion, was published posthumously in 1528. All three were printed by Dürer's friend, Hieronymus Andreä, who also produced the woodblocks. Andreä had begun cutting blocks for Dürer as early as 1515 and, with his staff, worked on the Maximilian projects (see cat. nos. 204–205). In Nuremberg, Andreä was known as Hieronymus "Formschneyder" (Hieronymus the Cutter).

Dürer made a major contribution to the development of scientific thought in Northern Europe during the early Renaissance through his essays on measurement and human proportion. Inspired by another friend, the learned humanist Willibald Pirckheimer and his distinguished circle of scholars, who had been educated at Italian universities, Dürer endeavored to educate his German contemporaries in the practical application of mathematics and perspective.

218–219

Underweysung der Messung, mit dem Zirckel und richtscheyt . . . (Teaching of Measurement with Compass and Ruler . . .)
Nuremberg, Hieronymus Formschneyder [Andreä], 1538

218
Meder XXVI, 1538, third German edition
Horatio Greenough Curtis Fund   Book Register 1650

The Roman Letters S T V X
Woodcut illustrations
Watermark: Imperial orb with monogram IG (M. 54)

Dürer's outstandingly lucid treatise on measurement re-affirms the tenets of Euclidian geometry and makes use of the discoveries of his Italian contemporaries. It was written to show how mathematics and geometry should be applied in art. Book I gives examples of linear geometry, from straight lines to curves, spirals, volutes, and conic sections. Book II discusses two-dimensional figures inscribed within curves or regular polygons; the forming of a pentagon on Ptolemaic principles; and how to show checkered pavements in perspective. Book III shows the use of linear geometry in architecture and decoration; typography; and offers three solutions for doubling a cube. Book IV treats the use of linear perspective for rendering three-dimensional forms.

Because of Dürer's concern that inscriptions on buildings should be easily read, the second part of Book III comprises Roman letters designed by Dürer and based on Italian forms (see *Albrecht Dürer*, pp. 347–348.). The clarity of the relationship between the letters and the text is both orderly and visually pleasing.

219
Meder XXVI, 1538, third German edition (incomplete copy)
Bound with Sebastien Münster, *Fürmalung und künstlich Beschreibung der Horologien*, Basel, Heinrich Peter, 1544
Coll.: A. F. J. Liel
Gift of Sylvester Rosa Koehler   K216

Draftsman Drawing a Vase
About 1527
Woodcut, B. 148
Watermark: Imperial orb (M. 60)

The posthumous edition of 1538 contains two additional woodcuts that had been designed by Dürer and inserted at the end of the treatise. This woodcut is derived from two pen drawings in the Dresden Sketchbook (W. 936 and W. 937), which, according to Panofsky, were probably done between 1510 and 1515. The idea for this draftsman's apparatus was borrowed from Jacob Keser but had practical limitations (see Panofsky, vol. 1, pg. 253).

Draftsman Drawing a Reclining Nude
About 1527
Woodcut, B. 149

Here a method of recording a foreshortened image is demonstrated. Panofsky states that such a device was already known to Italian artists but was probably not yet known to Northern artists. (For discussion of these devices, see Panofsky, vol. I, pp. 252–253.)

V

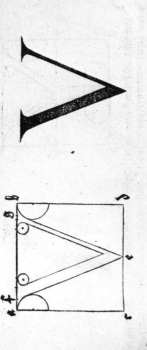

Das .v. mach also/ reyß zwo auffrechte lini .c.f. vnd .g.h. ein zehenteyl von der leng .a.b. hinder eñ für den seyten .a.c. vnd .b.d. Darnach/ zeuch des buchstaben zwen kreuz zůg/ den preyten das er oben hin vnd für das .c. vnd vnden hinden das .h. aber den dünnen zůg mach das er oben hin den seyten für das .c. vnd vnden für das .f. Darnach/ schweyff die zůg oben vnd vnden auß/ das fie nideren die vier eck .a.b.c.d. vnd noch den halben Diameter des grossern circkels dreyen eñ für den ein fünfteyl von der leng .a.b. Damit schweyff die vier weytern winckel auff/ aber des kleinern Diameters circkel mach preyt zwey drittel von des grössern zůge preyten.

Oder ander das .x. also/ alle ding laß beleyben wie für/ allein den dünnen strich reich oben vmb eyn halb teyl von des buchstaben preyten zůg mer auff/ so wirt das ober teyl kleiner vnd enger Dann das vn-der vnd sicht anderst dann für. Wie das hernach ist auffgeriffen.

X

Das .x. mach mitten vñ fein fierung in dem andrern halbteyl wie foren das .i. beschriben ist aber das ober halbteyl spalt von einander/ also das das sonder teyl zwey dritten/ vnd das hun-der ein drittentheyl haben von des buchstaben preyten zůg/ vñ keine fůr bede teyl auff bede seyten auß/ also das fie auffschweyssung die zwey eck .a.b. reychen vnd zů dem grossen circkel/ Dann du auffen die weytern winckel auffschweyff des Diameter des kleinern circkel mach preyt der fierung für neben dem buchstaben/ aber die Diameter der circkel in die kleinern winckel mach ein pentschen preyter Dann der geschalten zůg auf der selben seyten ist. Wie das hernach ist auffgeriffen.

$\zeta 4$

S

Das .s. stell auffrecht mitten in fein fierung/ vñ schweyff das vnden auff bedem seyten auß/ wie da foren das .i. gemacht ist/ Darnach fetz zwen punckten zetlichen ein zehenteyl von der leng .a.b. hinder das .a.c. vnd für das .b. ein .f. also lang mach/ den zwerch strich/ des buchstaben vñ der lini .a.b. aber bede seyten des zwerch zůge fetten auffgeschweyff werden/ vnd durch auffstrich abgeschnitten/ vnd oben füllen die selben schweyff ober die lini .a.b. gesogern vñ für die lini .a.b. lang. Darnach mach die vier eck .a.b.c.d. vnd noch den halben Diameter eines langen eñ für ein fünfteyl von der leng .a.b. lang. Darnach mach die.auffschweyssung/ durch zweyerley circkel/ yn dem engen winckeln brauch dich eines Diameters der zwey drittel hab/ von des buchstaben grossen preyten. Aber zů dem weyten winckel mach den Dia-meter so preyt a ist die seyten der fierung/ auff einem teyl neben dem preyten zůg des buchstaben.

Oder mach das .s. also in fein fierung/ mach den punckten .c. wie für hinder das .a. vnd schweyß den zwerch strich des buchstaben mit einem entstrich ab wie für/ vnd das die auffschweyffung nün halb so preyt fey als für/ vnd das vmb das oben ein fichlech eck peteyb/ die gleychen auff der anderen seyten auch/ aber den punckten .f. solff du vmb halbteyl nider zum .b. fetten vnd den abschneyd mpt seyner auff-schweyffung auffrichter vnd preyter machen Dann den foderen/ fünfftlaß all ding beleyben wie für. Wie ich das hernach hab auffgeriffen.

T

Das .t. mach also in fein fierung/ reyß .c.d. mit einem .e. mitten von einander. Darnach fetz ein punckt .f. ein zehenteyl von der leng .a.b. hinder das .a. also reyß fetz auch ein .g. für das .b. Darnach zeuch auch den preyten zůg des buchstaben von dem .f. grab mit feinen fpitz in das .c. vnd von dann zeuch den dünnen zůg oberlich biß an das .g. vnd schweyff die zůg oben auß/ wie das .a. foren beschreiben vnden auffgeschweyft ist. Wie das hernach ist auffgeriffen.

218. The Roman Letters S T V X from *Underweysung der Messung*

Item ob einer von einem kleinen bild / einem grossen risen an ein hohen thurn wund wolt malen) solt man dann so vil bappir zu samen leumen / das gros genug wär der zu einem gitter / wer verdroß sein vnd vngeschmackt / darumb mach sein gros gitter von bappir / sonder schneyb groß quadraten auf bappir als gros die sirrungen in deinem gitter solten seyn worden / darnach mach eyn sirrung nach der andern auf / wie dusem an zeisengt ist / wie zon die sirrungen wie sie nach einander geheren / Darnach leg sie zusamen wie ein karren ist / vnd so du an die mauren kumbst / magst du eyn platt nach dem andern auß machen / vn darfst du nicht wie sonst not ist / gantz verseychnen.

Zu dem freuntlichen leser.

Zum ende dise buches / So befent der erber man Albrecht Dürer mit seyner engere hand schrisst / zu der zeit / als er noch bey im leben / Das er seinem schülben so vil dem in disem buch an den eren und den weysen Bildhaubum Fürstkeymer gethan / ein ende wil geben / vnd mit der zeit / so im gott das leben verlyhe die bücher weil er von menschlicher proporcion / vnd andern darzu gehörig gesertiben / im truck lassen ausgeen / wie es dann von im selbe / vor seinem absterben mit vleiß ist gesche= hen. Auch nachmals auf gerugsamer vertegung Agnes Dürerin seiner nachgelassne wittib / in= gleich latein gebracht / auf das solchs ires haußwirts kunst und arbeyt / auch andern / welchen teutsche sprach vnbekandt / zu nutze möcht reychen. Darumb soll menigklich gewarnet sein / dise buch in keinen wege nach zutrucken bey pеen vnd straff / so verdische von Kayserlicher Maiestat / streyben an ansengen / darnach mag sich yetlicher richten / Gott den herren sey lobe vnd ers vigt sich Amen.

Getruckt Zu Nürmberg durch Hieronymum Formschneyber.
Anno. M. D. XXXVIIIJ.

Item noch ein anderen brauch zu Conterfeten / darduch man eyn yelliche Corpus mag grösser oder kleyner abconterfeten wie vil man wil / desshalben nützlicher dan mit dem glas darumb das es freier ist / Darzu soll man haben ein ram mit einem gitter von stanstern schwarzen zwiren gemacht / dir lassen oder sirrungen eine vngefertlich zweyer finger breyt / Darnach soll man haben ein absehen oben zugespizu also gemacht / das man es höher oder nibrer richten mag / Das bedeur das aug mit dem o. Darnach leg hynauls in zimlicher weiten dz corpus so du conterfeten wilt / ruscs vnd preuge nach deinem wollen / vn gee als weg sunderslich vnd hab dein aug zu dem absehen u. in dem absehen o. meßt darnum / vnd besihe das Corpus wie es dir gesält / vn ob es recht nach deinem willen ligt / Darnach stell dz gitter oder ram zwischen dem Corpus vnd deinem absehen also / wilt du wenig luffen oder sirrungen begreiffen oder sirrungen begreissen / so ruсk es boff näher zu dem Corpus / Darnach besich wie vil dz corpus im gitter luffen begreift nach leng vn breyten / Darnach reiß ein gitter gros oder klein auf ein bappir oder tasel darein du conterfeten wilt / vnd sich hin über dein aug.o. des spis am absehen auf das Corpus / vnd was du in yder sirrung des gitters findest / das trag in dein gitter das du auf dem bappir hast das ist gut vnd gerecht / Wilt du aber für das sirsig absehen ein löche machen / darduch du sihest ist den so gar solcher meynung hab ich hernach ein form aufgeriffen.

219. Draftsman Drawing a Vase *and* Draftsman Drawing a Nude from *Underweysung der Messung*

276

220

Etliche underricht, zu befestigung der Stett, Schloss und flecken (Treatise on the Fortification of Towns, Castles, and Places)
Nuremberg [Hieronymus Andreä], October, 1527

Meder XXVIII, 1527, first German edition, A
Bound with *Underweysung der messung,* Nuremberg, 1525
Coll.: Dr. Lautensack
Samuel Putnam Avery Fund   Book Register 2973, 38.1618

Design for a Gun Carriage
About 1527
Woodcut illustration, fold out
Watermark: Bear (M. 95)

In his treatise on fortification dedicated to Emperor Maximilian's grandson Ferdinand, Dürer offered plans for the construction of defenses against the warring Turks and for organizing an ideal, easily defended city. Chapters I, II, and III discuss different ways of building forts; chapter IV deals with the defense and fortification of castles; chapter V describes the defense of a mountain pass with a fort; and chapter VI recommends the use of surrounding walls as the best form of security for an old town; chapter VII deals with artillery.

Although most of his ideas were derived from a number of fifteenth- and sixteenth-century sources, it has been suggested that Dürer invented the "polygonal *tracé*" system (see Conway, p. 271). Two forts were built in Strassburg on this principle: Kronenburg Gate and Roseneck.

One of Dürer's large woodcuts, "Seige of a Fortress" (B. 137, not exhibited) is certainly related to this book and, on rare occasions, has been bound into the first and second editions.

The gun carriage woodcut is based on a small sketch in the British Museum (Dürer Manuscript, II); illustrated in Hans Tietze and Erika Tietze-Conrat, *Kritisches Verzeichnis der Werke Albrecht Dürers* [Augsburg, Basel, and Leipzig, 1938], vol. 2, part 2, p. 204, no. 969.

221

Hierinn sind begriffen vier Bücher von menschlicher Proportion ... (Herein Are Concepts of the Four Books on Human Proportion ...)
Arnheim, Johann Janssen, 1603

Meder XXIX, 1603, second German edition
Published in *Opera Alberti Dureri (Works by Albrecht Dürer)*
Arnheim, Johann Janssen, 1604
Meder XXVI, 1604, fourth German edition (incomplete copy)
Gift of Thomas Gaffield   Book Register 480   M2852

Male Model Inscribed in a Circle
Woodcut illustration
Watermark: Coat-of-arms of Saxony (M. 191)

The volume on human proportion grew out of earlier studies on ideal proportion, such as those that resulted in the engraved *Fall of Man* of 1504 (cat. no. 84). More notes and drafts exist for this book than for any of Dürer's other writings. In his book he expanded the theory of proportion of the first-century architect Vitruvius to establish a flexible system of measurement. Dürer's figures were arrived at by actually measuring hundreds of living people of differing sizes. Book I discusses measurements of male and female heads, hands, and feet and those for babies. Book II introduces eight additional types, such as tall, short, thin, fat, considered with respect to the canons of measurement of the fifteenth-century Italian artist Alberti. Book III treats the mathematical variations of basic proportions and several grotesque anatomies. Book IV describes the use of perspective and geometry in analyzing human movement.

This book was Dürer's most original effort; he strove toward workable types and variations of human proportion rather than inflexible ideals.

The Arnheim publication of his three books was a reprint of the first edition of each treatise, without any of the subsequent corrections.

The woodcut exhibited is from Book II.

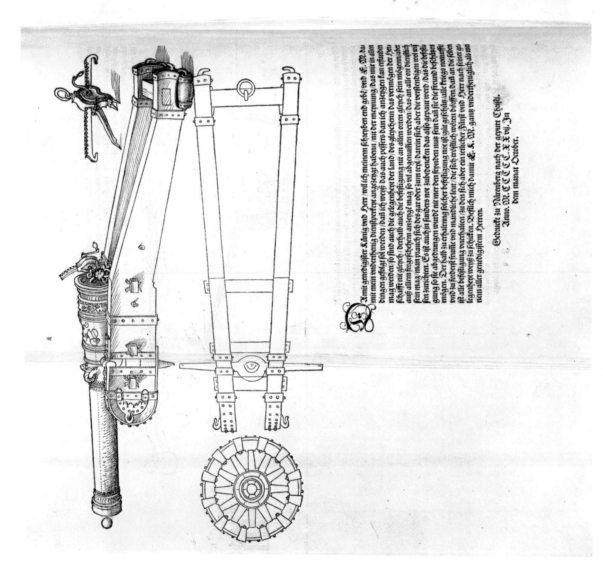

220. Design for a Gun Carriage from *Befestigung*

221. Male Model Inscribed in a Circle from *Vier Bücher von Menschlicher Proportion*

GLOSSARY

For further information on printmaking techniques and Dürer's application of them, see the Introduction.

Biting (Bitten). The action of acid on the exposed metal of an etching plate to form the grooves that will receive the printer's ink (*see* **Etching**).

Burin. A tool used to incise the lines of an engraving. It consists of a faceted steel bar ground obliquely to a sharp point and set into a wooden handle (*see* **Engraving**).

Burr. A ridge of metal that is raised up beside the line when an engraving or drypoint line is incised or scratched into the printing plate. In engraving, the burr is usually removed from the line before printing. *Drypoint burr* is usually retained and is more prominent than engraved burr. Drypoint burr is, however, very fragile and wears away rapidly with the pressure of repeated printing.

Chiaroscuro Woodcut. A woodcut in which more than one block is used in order to render tones of light and shadow, often in color (*see* **Woodcut**).

Clean Wiping. *See* **Inking and Wiping.**

Cross-Hatching. *See* **Hatching.**

Drypoint. In a drypoint, the lines that receive the ink and that print are freely scratched into the metal printing plate with a sharp point (*see* **Intaglio**).

Drypoint Burr. *See* **Burr.**

Electrotype. A duplicate printing surface made by electrically coating with metal a mold of the original printing surface.

Engraving. In an engraving, the lines that receive the ink and that print are incised into the copper printing plate with a special tool called a burin (*see* **Burin; Intaglio**).

Etching. In etching, the metal printing plate is covered with a *ground* that is resistant to acid. The lines are drawn in the ground with an *etching needle*, exposing the metal, which is then *bitten* with acid to form the grooves that receive the printer's ink (*see* **Biting; Intaglio**).

Etching Needle. *See* **Etching.**

Foxing. Brownish spots caused by fungus which sometimes discolor the paper on which a print is printed.

Ground. *See* **Etching.**

Hatching. Parallel shading or modeling lines. When such lines cross or intersect each other, this is referred to as *cross-hatching*.

Impression. A single printing from a printing plate or block (*see* **Printing**).

Inking and Wiping. When the image on an intaglio printing plate (engraving, etching, drypoint) is completed, the plate is inked for printing. Ink is forced into the grooves and the surface of the plate is then *wiped clean* of excess ink. Wiping the plate often produces fine *wiping scratches* on the polished surface of the plate. In a *tonal inking* of the plate, a film of ink is left on the plate surface and prints as a gray tone. *Selective inking and wiping* means that the ink has been intentionally left on or wiped away from specific areas of the plate.

Intaglio. In intaglio prints, the lines that receive the ink and that print are below the surface of the metal printing plate. Engraving, etching, and drypoint are all intaglio methods of printmaking.

Plate mark. *See* **Printing.**

Printing. When a printing plate or block is inked and ready for printing, it is placed in the printing press, covered with a sheet of paper, and an impression is *printed (pulled, taken)* under great pressure. During the printing, the edges of an intaglio plate (engraving, etching, drypoint) make an indentation in the paper which is called the *plate mark*.

State. Whenever changes are made in a printing block or plate and new impressions are printed, this is described in print catalogues as a "change of state."

Stereotype. A metal cast made from a mold taken from a relief printing surface, such as a woodblock. *See also* **Woodcut**.

Selective Inking and Wiping. *See* **Inking and Wiping.**

Tonal Inking. *See* **Inking and Wiping.**

Wiping. *See* **Inking and Wiping.**

Woodblock. *See* **Woodcut.**

Woodcut. In the woodcut printmaking process, the spaces that read as white areas in the printed image are cut away from the *woodblock* with a knife. The lines that receive the ink and that print are left standing in relief on the surface of the block. *See also* **Chiaroscuro Woodcut.**

Watermark. The handmade papers of Dürer's time were formed on wire screens. The paper maker was sometimes identified by a watermark in the sheet of paper. A watermark is created by bending wire into a symbol and attaching it to the screen. The paper fibers are thinner over this wire, and the watermark therefore reads as a translucent image in the paper when held against the light.

SELECTED BIBLIOGRAPHY

In addition to the books for which short titles were given, the authors made use of the following sources:

Bernheimer, Richard. *Wild Men in the Middle Ages.* Cambridge, 1952.

Brunner, Felix. *A Handbook of Graphic Reproduction Processes.* New York, 1962.

Davies, Hugh W. *Catalogue of a Collection of Early German Books in the Library of C. Fairfax Murray.* 2 vols. London, 1913.

Dodgson, Campbell. *Albrecht Dürer, Engravings and Etchings.* London, 1926.
—*Catalogue of Early German and Flemish Woodcuts in the British Museum.* 2 vols. London, 1903. Vol. 1, 1903.

Hausmann, Oberbaurath B. *Albrecht Dürer's Kupferstiche, Radirungen, Holzschnitte und Zeichnungen.* Hanover, 1861.

Heller, Joseph. *Das Leben und die Werke Albrecht Dürer's.* 2 vols. Leipzig, 1831. Vol. 2, 1831.

Hind, Arthur M. *History of Woodcut.* 2 vols. Boston and New York, 1935.

Hoyt, Anna C. "A Dürer Proof Discovered." *Boston Museum Bulletin,* L (1952), 10–11.

Ivins, William M., Jr. "Notes on Three Dürer Woodblocks." *Metropolitan Museum Studies,* II (1929–1930), 102–111.

Koehler, S. R. *A Chronological Catalogue of the Engravings, Dry-points and Etchings of Albrecht Dürer.* New York, 1897.

Kurth, Willi. *The Complete Woodcuts of Albrecht Dürer.* Translated by S. M. Welsh. 1927. Reprint. New York, 1963.

Lange, K., and Fuhse, F. *Dürers Schriftlicher Nachlass.* Halle, 1893.

Museum of Fine Arts, Boston. *Exhibition of Albert Dürer's Engravings, Etchings, and Dry-points, and of Most of the Woodcuts Executed from His Designs.* Catalogue by S. R. Koehler. Boston, 1888.

Philadelphia Museum of Art. *Albrecht Dürer, A Study Exhibition of Print Connoisseurship.* Catalogue by Richard S. Field. Philadelphia, 1970.

Ragusa, Isa. trans. *Meditations on the Life of Christ.* Princeton, 1961.

Robbins, Rossell Hope. *The Enclyclopedia of Witchcraft and Demonology.* New York, 1959.

Rossiter, H. P. "Maxmilian's Triumphal Arch." *Boston Museum Bulletin,* XLIX (1951), 95–98.
—"Two Dry-points by Dürer." *Boston Museum Bulletin,* XXXVI (1938), 36.

Ruzicka, Rudolph, and Ivins, W. M., Jr. "Contemporary Prints from Dürer's Woodblocks." *Bulletin of the Metropolitan Museum of Art,* XVI (1921), 53–55.

Thausing, Moriz. *Albert Dürer: His Life and Works.* 2 vols. Translated by Fred A. Eaton. London, 1882.

The Apocryphal New Testament. Translated by Montague Rhodes James. 1924. Reprint. Oxford, 1960.

The Book of the Wanderings of Brother Felix Fabri. Vol. 1, pt. 2. Translated by Aubrey Stewart. London, 1892.

Tietze, Hans, and Tietze-Conrat, Erika. *Kritisches Verzeichnis der Werke Albrecht Dürers.* 2 vols. (vol. 2 in 2 parts). Augsburg, Basel, and Leipzig, 1928–1938.

Trens, Manuel. *María Iconografía de la Virgen en el Arte Espanol.* Madrid, 1946.

Vasari, Giorgio. *Lives of the Painters, Sculptors, and Architects.* 6 vols. London, 1890–1892. Vol. 3, translated by Mrs. Jonathan Foster, 1891.

Wegner, Wolfgang. "Eisenradierung." In *Reallexicon zur deutschen Kunstgeschichte.* Stuttgart, 1937–. Vol. 4, 1958, 1139–1151.

PRINTS AND ILLUSTRATED BOOKS BY ALBRECHT DÜRER IN THE MUSEUM OF FINE ARTS, BOSTON

October 30, 1971

The prints and illustrated books listed here are those catalogued by Joseph Meder as being by Dürer. Prints classified by Meder as "School of Dürer," as copies, and as facsimile reproductions have been omitted. The list has been compiled according to Bartsch, who divided Dürer's prints into two groups by medium: intaglio (engravings, etchings, and drypoints) and woodcut. Within these groups, the prints are arranged, as in Bartsch, according to subject matter. Prints not described by Bartsch in his catalogue or appendix are placed at the end, following Meder's order. Illustrated books are listed separately by order of date of publication. This system is the one presently used by the Department of Prints and Drawings for storing Dürer material.

Meder's numbers and classifications further categorize the impressions. Individual impressions are identified by donor or purchase fund and Museum accession number. As in the catalogue entries, Panofsky's titles are generally used.

Asterisks denote prints and books discussed and reproduced in the exhibition catalogue.

Engravings, Etchings, and Drypoints

B.1   The Fall of Man (Adam and Eve)
   *M.1, II, a
   Centennial Gift of Landon T. Clay (68.187)
   M.1, II, b
   Bequest of Harriet J. Bradbury (M31963)
   M.1, II, c
   Harvey D. Parker Collection (P246)
   *M.1, III, a
   Harvey D. Parker Collection (P247)

B.2   The Nativity
   M.2b-c
   Katherine Eliot Bullard Fund (1971.218)
   *M.2c-d
   Harvey D. Parker Collection (P248)
   *M.2c-f
   Frederick Keppel Memorial Bequest, by sale of duplicates
      (68.270)

B.3   Man of Sorrows by the Column (Engraved Passion)
   *M.3b-c
   Gift of Edward Habich (M8835)

B.4   Agony in the Garden (Engraved Passion)
   *M.4c
   Gift of Edward Habich (M8836)

B.5   Betrayal of Christ (Engraved Passion)
   *M.5c
   Gift of Edward Habich (M8837)

B.6   Christ before Caiaphas (Engraved Passion)
   *M.6a
   Gift of Edward Habich (M8838)

B.7   Christ before Pilate for the First Time (Engraved Passion)
   *M.7c
   Gift of Edward Habich (M8839)

B.8   Flagellation of Christ (Engraved Passion)
   *M.8c
   Gift of Edward Habich (M8840)

B.9   Christ Crowned with Thorns (Engraved Passion)
   *M.9b
   Gift of Edward Habich (M8841)

B.10   Ecce Homo (Engraved Passion)
   *M.10b
   Gift of Edward Habich (M8842)

B.11   Pilate Washing His Hands (Engraved Passion)
   *M.11a
   Gift of Edward Habich (M8843)

B.12   Bearing of the Cross (Engraved Passion)
   *M.12b
   Gift of Edward Habich (M8844)
   *M.12b-c
   Gift of Mrs. Samuel Cabot (51.2403)

B.13   Crucifixion (Engraved Passion)
   *M.13d
   Gift of Edward Habich (M8845)

B.14   Lamentation (Engraved Passion)
   *M.14a-b
   Gift of Edward Habich (M8846)

B.15   Deposition of Christ (Engraved Passion)
   *M.15c (?)
   Gift of Edward Habich (M8847)

B.16   Harrowing of Hell (Engraved Passion)
   *M.16c
   Gift of Edward Habich (M8848)

B.17   Resurrection (Engraved Passion)
   *M.17c
   Gift of Edward Habich   (M8849)

B.18   Saints Peter and John Healing the Lame Man
   M.18a
   Gift of Edward Habich (M8850)
   M.18a
   Gift of William Norton Bullard (M29847)

B.19   Agony in the Garden
   *M.19, before rust marks, a-c
   Katherine Eliot Bullard Fund (68.206)

M.19, before rust marks, b–c
Gift of William Norton Bullard (M29848)

*M.19, with rust marks, b
Harvey D. Parker Collection (P281)

B.20 Man of Sorrows with Arms Outstretched
M.20a–c
Stephen Bullard Memorial Fund (68.235)

B.21 Man of Sorrows with Hands Bound
M.21a–b
Maria Antoinette Evans Fund (M32598)
M.21d
Harvey D. Parker Collection (P283)

B.22 Man of Sorrows Seated
*M.22, I, c
Gift of Landon T. Clay and Guido R. Perera (68.198)
M.22, I, c
Harvey D. Parker Collection (P284)

B.23 The Crucifixion (Roundel)
*M.24, I
Harriet Otis Cruft Fund (22.1063)

B.24 Crucifixion
M.23a–b
Katherine Eliot Bullard Fund (68.203)

B.25 The Sudarium Displayed by Two Angels
*M.26b
Stephen Bullard Memorial Fund (44.820)
M.26c (?)
Harvey D. Parker Collection (P288)

B.26 The Sudarium Spread Out by an Angel
*M.27, before rust marks, c
Harvey D. Parker Collection (P289)
M.27, before rust marks, c
Katherine Eliot Bullard Fund (68.207)

B.28 The Prodigal Son amid the Swine
*M.28a
Seth K. Sweetser Fund (32.537)
*M.28b
Centennial Gift of Landon T. Clay (68.181)
*M.28b
Harvey D. Parker Collection (P291)

B.29 The Virgin Mary with the Infant Jesus and Saint Ann
M.43a
Gift of Henry P. Rossiter (55.565)
M.43a
Harvey D. Parker Collection (P292)

B.30 The Virgin on the Crescent
M.29b(?)
Stephen Bullard Memorial Fund (44.819)
M.29d
Harvey D. Parker Collection (P293)

B.31 The Virgin on the Crescent with a Crown of Stars
M.32, II, b
Katherine Eliot Bullard Fund (68.202)

B.32 The Virgin on the Crescent with a Crown of Stars and a Scepter
*M.37a
Horatio Greenough Curtis Fund (51.728)
M.37a
Harvey D. Parker Collection (P296)

B.33 The Virgin on the Crescent with a Diadem
M.35a
Gift of William Norton Bullard (M29849)
M.35a
Harvey D. Parker Collection (P297)
M.35b–c
Sylvester R. Koehler Collection (K95)

B.34 Madonna on a Grassy Bench
*M.31a
Katherine Eliot Bullard Fund (1971.70)
M.31a(?)
Harvey D. Parker Collection (P298)

B.35 Madonna by the Tree
M.34c
Harvey D. Parker Collection (P299)

B.36 Madonna Nursing
M.39b
Harvey D. Parker Collection (P301)
M.39b(?)
Gift of William Norton Bullard (M29850)

B.37 Madonna Crowned by an Angel
M.41, with the stroke, a
Stephen Bullard Memorial Fund (68.237)
M.41, with the stroke, a
Harvey D. Parker Collection (P302)

B.38 Madonna with the Swaddled Infant
M.40b
Harvey D. Parker Collection (P303)

B.39 Madonna Crowned by Two Angels
M.38b–c
Harvey D. Parker Collection (P304)

B.40 Madonna by the Wall
*M.36, I, b
Katherine Eliot Bullard Fund (68.205)

B.41 The Madonna with the Pear
*M.33a
Katherine Eliot Bullard Fund (68.204)
M.33b
Harvey D. Parker Collection (P306)

B.42 The Madonna with the Monkey
*M.30a
Gift of Miss Ellen T. Bullard (M30789)

M.30d
Harvey D. Parker Collection (P307)

M.30l(?)
Frederick Keppel Memorial Bequest, by sale of duplicates
(68.268)

**B.43 Holy Family with Saint John, The Magdalen,
and Nicodemus**

*M.44, before the stroke, a–b
Anna Mitchell Richards Fund (M33781)

*M.44, with the stroke partly polished away, c
Harvey D. Parker Fund (68.260)

M.44, with the stroke partly polished away, c
Harvey D. Parker Collection (P308)

B.44 Holy Family with the Butterfly

*M.42e
Harvey D. Parker Collection (P309)

B.46 Saint Philip

*M.48a
Centennial Gift of Landon T. Clay (68.192)

B.47 Saint Bartholomew

M.45a
Harvey D. Parker Collection (P312)

B.48 Saint Thomas

*M.50b
Centennial Gift of Landon T. Clay (68.190)

B.49 Saint Simon

M.49a–b
Gift of the Estate of George R. Nutter (M33984)

M.49a–b
Harvey D. Parker Collection (P314)

B.50 Saint Paul

M.47, II, a–b
Centennial Gift of Landon T. Clay (68.191)

B.51 Saint Christopher

*M.53a
Harvey D. Parker Collection (P316)

B.52 Saint Christopher

M.52b
Harvey D. Parker Collection (P317)

B.53 Saint George on Foot

M.55b(?)
Harvey D. Parker Collection (P318)

B.54 Saint George on Horseback

M.56b
Gift of Miss Ellen T. Bullard (M30791)

M.56d
Harvey D. Parker Collection (P319)

B.55 Saint Sebastian at the Tree

M.62b
Harvey D. Parker Collection (P320)

B.56 Saint Sebastian Tied to a Column

M.61, I
Harvey D. Parker Collection (P321)

B.57 Saint Eustace

*M.60b
Gift at the request of Miss Ellen T. Bullard (59.803)

M.60c
Harvey D. Parker Collection (P322)

Worn impression on satin
Frederick Keppel Memorial Bequest, by sale of duplicates
(68.269)

B.58 Saint Anthony

*M.51a
Gift of William Norton Bullard (M29851)

B.59 Saint Jerome by the Pollard Willow

*M.58, II, a
Anna Mitchell Richards Fund (M33780)

*M.58, II, c–d
Gift of Richard H. Zinser (M.App.)

M.58, III, a
Harvey D. Parker Collection (P3369)

B.60 Saint Jerome in his Study

*M.59a
Gift of Mrs. W. Scott Fitz (M29037)

*M.59b
Gift of Mrs. Henry P. Kidder (37.353)

B.61 Saint Jerome in Penitence

M.57b–d
Harvey D. Parker Collection (P327)

M.57b–e
Katherine Eliot Bullard Fund (68.199)

B.63 The Penance of Saint John Chrysostom

*M.54b–c
Harvey D. Parker Collection (P328)

B.66 Three Putti

M.99b
Horatio Greenough Curtis Fund (44.607)

M.99c
Harvey D. Parker Collection (P330)

**B.67 Witch Riding Backwards on a Goat, Accompanied
by Four Putti**

*M.68, I, b
Gift of Miss Ellen T. Bullard (M30790)

M.68, I, b
Harvey D. Parker Collection (P331)

B.68 Apollo and Diana

M.64b–c
Gift of Lee M. Friedman (58.1050)

M.64b–c
Harvey D. Parker Collection (P332)

B.69 Musical Satyr and Nymph with Baby (Satyr's Family)

*M.65b
Harvey D. Parker Collection (P333)

B.70 "The Desperate Man"

M.95a–c
Harvey D. Parker Collection (P334)

B.96 The Small Horse

M.93a
Harvey D. Parker Collection (P362)

*M.93a
George W. Wales Collection (M1743)

B.97 The Large Horse

*M.94a
Harvey D. Parker Collection (P363)

B.98 Knight, Death, and the Devil

*M.74a
Harvey D. Parker Fund (68.261)

M.74b(?)
Gift of Miss Ellen T. Bullard (M30792)

*M.74b(?)
Bequest of Mrs. Horatio G. Curtis (27.1353)

*M.74d
Gift at the Request of Miss Ellen T. Bullard (59.804)

B.99 The Landscape with the Cannon

*M.96, before rust marks, a
Katherine Eliot Bullard Fund (68.209)

M.96, with rust marks, b–c
Harvey D. Parker Collection (P365)

B.100 Coat-of-Arms with the Cock

M.97c–d
Stephen Bullard Memorial Fund (68.236)

M.97c–d
Harvey D. Parker Collection (P366)

B.101 Coat-of-Arms of Death

*M.98b
Gift of William Norton Bullard (M29853)

M.98c
Harvey D. Parker Collection (P367)

B.102 Cardinal Albrecht of Brandenburg

M.100, I, a
Harvey D. Parker Collection (P368)

B.103 Cardinal Albrecht of Brandenburg

*M.101, I, b
Maria Antoinette Evans Fund (M32599)

*M.101, II
Harvey D. Parker Collection (P369)

B.104 Frederich the Wise, Elector of Saxony

M.102a
Harvey D. Parker Collection (P370)

B.105 Philip Melanchthon

*M.104a
Stephen Bullard Memorial Fund (68.238)

M.104c(?)
Harvey D. Parker Collection (P372)

B.106 Willibald Pirckheimer

M.103, I, b–c
Harvey D. Parker Collection (P373)

B.107 Erasmus of Rotterdam

M.105d(?)
Sumner Bequest (M84)

Woodcuts

B.1 Cain Slaying Abel

M.106b
Maria Antoinette Evans Fund (M32600)

B.2 Samson Rending the Lion

*M.107a
Bequest of Francis Bullard (M24883a)

M.107g
Harvey D. Parker Collection (P1)

*Electrotype impression
Gift of the Trustees of the Metropolitan Museum of Art
(M28468)

B.3 Adoration of the Magi

*M.208a
Katherine Eliot Bullard Fund (1971.71)

M.208f
Harvey D. Parker Collection (P2)

B.4 Man of Sorrows, Mocked by a Soldier (Large Passion)

*M.113, before the text edition
Stephen Bullard Memorial Fund (68.240)

*M.113, 1511 edition with Latin text
Gift of Mrs. Horatio G. Curtis, by sale of duplicates (68.248)

M.113, after 1511, without text, b
Harvey D. Parker Collection (P218)

M.113, after 1511, without text, d
Gift of Robert Treat Paine, Jr. (50.2651)

B.5 Last Supper (Large Passion)

*M.114, before the text edition
Bequest of Francis Bullard (M24867)

*M.114, before the text edition
Stephen Bullard Memorial Fund (68.241)

M.114, 1511 edition with Latin text
Bequest of Mrs. Horatio G. Curtis, by sale of duplicates
(68.249)

B.6 Agony in the Garden (Large Passion)

*M.115, before the text edition, a
Stephen Bullard Memorial Fund (68.242)

M.115, 1511 edition with Latin text
Bequest of Mrs. Horatio G. Curtis, by sale of duplicates
(68.250)

M.115, after 1511, without text, b
Bequest of Francis Bullard (M24868)

B.7 Betrayal of Christ (Large Passion)

*M.116, before the text edition
Bequest of Francis Bullard (M24869)

M.116, 1511 edition with Latin text
Bequest of Mrs. Horatio G. Curtis, by sale of duplicates
(68.251)

B.8 Flagellation of Christ (Large Passion)

*M.117, before the text edition
Bequest of Francis Bullard (M24870)

*M.117, 1511 edition with Latin text
Bequest of Mrs. Horatio G. Curtis, by sale of duplicates
(68.252)

*M.117, after 1511, without text, d
Harvey D. Parker Collection (P222)

B.9 Ecce Homo (Large Passion)

*M.118, before the text edition, b
Harvey D. Parker Collection (P223)

M.118, 1511 edition with Latin text
Bequest of Mrs. Horatio G. Curtis, by sale of duplicates
(68.253)

M.118, after 1511, without text, a–b
Bequest of Francis Bullard (M24871)

B.10 Bearing of the Cross (Large Passion)

*M.119, before the text edition
Bequest of Francis Bullard (M24872)

M.119, 1511 edition with Latin text
Bequest of Mrs. Horatio G. Curtis, by sale of duplicates
(68.254)

*M.119, 1511 edition with Latin text, contemporary coloring
Gift of the Estate of George R. Nutter, by sale of duplicates
(68.275)

B.11 Crucifixion (Large Passion)

M.120, before the text edition, a
Harvey D. Parker Collection (P225)

*M.120, before the text edition, b
Bequest of Francis Bullard (M24873)

M.120, 1511 edition with Latin text
Bequest of Mrs. Horatio G. Curtis, by sale of duplicates
(68.255)

*M.120, after 1511, without text, b–d
Bequest of Francis Bullard (M24874)

B.12 Deposition of Christ (Large Passion)

*M.123, before the text edition
Bequest of Francis Bullard (M24875)

M.123, before the text edition
Harvey D. Parker Collection (P226)

M.123, 1511 edition with Latin text
Bequest of Mrs. Horatio G. Curtis, by sale of duplicates
(68.256)

B.13 Lamentation (Large Passion)

*M.122, before the text edition, a
Bequest of Francis Bullard (M24876)

M.122, before the text edition, b
Stephen Bullard Memorial Fund (68.243)

M.122, 1511 edition with Latin text
Bequest of Mrs. Horatio G. Curtis, by sale of duplicates
(68.257)

B.14 Harrowing of Hell (Large Passion)

*M.121, before the text edition, b
Bequest of Francis Bullard (M24877)

M.121, before the text edition, b
Harvey D. Parker Collection (P228)

M.121, 1511 edition with Latin text
Bequest of Mrs. Horatio G. Curtis, by sale of duplicates
(68.258)

B.15 Resurrection (Large Passion)

*M.124, before the text edition, b
Bequest of Francis Bullard (M24878)

M.124, 1511 edition with Latin text
Bequest of Mrs. Horatio G. Curtis, by sale of duplicates
(68.259)

B.16 Man of Sorrows Seated (Small Passion)

*M.125, 1511 edition with Latin text
Centennial Gift of Landon T. Clay (68.193)

B.17 The Fall of Man (Small Passion)

*M.126, after 1511, without text, a–b
Gift of Mrs. C. Tunnard in Memory of W. G. Russell Allen
(61.1354)

M.126, after 1511, without text, a–b
Harvey D. Parker Collection (P16)

B.18 Expulsion from Paradise (Small Passion)

*M.127, after 1511, without text, c
Harvey D. Parker Collection (P17)

B.19 Annunciation (Small Passion)

*M.128, before the text edition
Harvey D. Parker Collection (P18)

B.20 Nativity (Small Passion)

*M.129, before the text edition
Harvey D. Parker Collection (P19)

B.21 Christ Taking Leave from His Mother (Small Passion)

*M.132, before the text edition
Harvey D. Parker Collection (P20)

B.22 Entry into Jerusalem (Small Passion)

*M.130, before the text edition
Harvey D. Parker Collection (P21)

M.130, after 1511, without text, a
Gift of Mrs. C. Tunnard in memory of W. G. Russell Allen
(61.1355)

**B.23 Christ Driving the Money Lenders from the Temple
(Small Passion)**

*M.131, before the text edition
Harvey D. Parker Collection (P22)

B.24 Last Supper (Small Passion)

*M.133, before the text edition
Harvey D. Parker Collection (P23)

B.25 Christ Washing the Feet of the Disciples (Small Passion)

*M.134, before the text edition
Harvey D. Parker Collection (P24)

B.26 Agony in the Garden (Small Passion)

*M.135, before the text edition
Harvey D. Parker Collection (P25)

B.27 Betrayal of Christ (Small Passion)

*M.136, before the text edition
Harvey D. Parker Collection (P26)

B.28 Christ before Annas (Small Passion)

*M.137, before the text edition
Harvey D. Parker Collection (P27)

M.183, II, b
Horatio G. Curtis Fund (M31654)

B.58 Crucifixion

M.182, II, d
Harvey D. Parker Collection (P230)

M.182, Derschau printing
Bequest of W. G. Russell Allen (64.791)

B.59 Calvary

M.180, I, e
Bequest of Francis Bullard (M24882)

**B.60 Virgin Mary Appearing to Saint John on Patmos
(Title page to the Apocalypse)**

M.163, 1498 edition with Latin text
Gift of Edward P. Warren (M9404)

*M.163, 1511 edition with Latin text
Bequest of William P. Babcock (B95)

B.61 Martyrdom of Saint John (Apocalypse)

*M.164, before the text edition
Bequest of Francis Bullard (M24883)

*M.164, 1498 edition with Latin text
Gift of Edward P. Warren (M9405)

M.164, 1511 edition with Latin text
Bequest of William P. Babcock (B96)

B.62 The Vision of the Seven Candlesticks (Apocalypse)

*M.165, 1498 edition with Latin text
Gift of Edward P. Warren (M9406)

M.165, 1511 edition with Latin text
Bequest of William P. Babcock (B97)

B.63 Saint John before God and the Elders (Apocalypse)

*M.166, 1498 edition with Latin text
Gift of Edward P. Warren (M9407)

B.64 The Four Horsemen (Apocalypse)

*M.167, before the text edition, b
Bequest of Francis Bullard (M24884)

M.167, 1498 edition with German text
Bequest of Francis Bullard (M24885)

M.167, 1498 edition with Latin text
Gift of Edward P. Warren (M9408)

M.167, 1511 edition with Latin text
Bequest of William P. Babcock (B100)

B.65 The Opening of the Fifth and Sixth Seals (Apocalypse)

*M.168, 1498 edition with Latin text
Gift of Edward P. Warren (M9409)

*M.168, 1511 edition with Latin text
Bequest of William P. Babcock (B101)

B.66 The Four Angels Holding the Winds (Apocalypse)

*M.169, 1498 edition with German text
Bequest of Francis Bullard (M24886)

M.169, 1498 edition with Latin text
Gift of Edward P. Warren (M9410)

M.169, 1511 edition with Latin text
Harvey D. Parker Collection (P98)

B.67 The Adoration of the Lamb (Apocalypse)

*M.176, 1498 edition with Latin text
Gift of Edward P. Warren (M9417)

B.68 The Seven Trumpets (Apocalypse)

*M.170, 1498 edition with Latin text
Gift of Edward P. Warren (M9411)

B.69 The Four Avenging Angels (Apocalypse)

*M.171, 1498 edition with Latin text
Gift of Edward P. Warren (M9412)

*M.171, 1511 edition with Latin text
Bequest of William P. Babcock (B106)

M.171, 1511 edition with Latin text
Bequest of Francis Bullard (M24887)

B.70 Saint John Devouring the Book (Apocalypse)

*M.172, 1498 edition with Latin text
Gift of Edward P. Warren (M9413)

M.172, 1498 edition with German text
Bequest of Francis Bullard (M24888)

B.71 The Apocalyptic Woman (Apocalypse)

*M.173, 1498 edition with Latin text
Gift of Edward P. Warren (M9414)

M.173, 1511 edition with Latin text
Gift of William Norton Bullard (B108)

B.72 Saint Michael Fighting the Dragon (Apocalypse)

*M.174, 1498 edition with Latin text
Gift of Edward P. Warren (M9415)

B.73 The Babylonian Whore (Apocalypse)

*M.177, before the text edition
Bequest of Francis Bullard (M24889)

M.177, 1498 edition with Latin text
Gift of Edward P. Warren (M9418)

M.177, 1511 edition with Latin text
Gift of William Norton Bullard (B110)

B.74 The Beast with Two Horns Like a Lamb (Apocalypse)

M.175, before the text edition
Bequest of Francis Bullard (M24890)

*M.175, 1498 edition with Latin text
Gift of Edward P. Warren (M9416)

*M.175, after 1511, without text
Bequest of Charles Sumner (M21330)

B.75 The Angel with the Key of the Bottomless Pit (Apocalypse)

*M.178, 1498 edition with Latin text (?)
Gift of Edward P. Warren (M9419)

B.76 Madonna on the Crescent (Life of the Virgin)

*M.188, before the text edition
Maria Antoinette Evans Fund (M32092)

*M.188, 1511 edition with Latin text
Katherine Eliot Bullard Fund (68.213)

M.188, after 1511, without text, e
Harvey D. Parker Collection (P109)

B.77 Rejection of Joachim's Offering (Life of the Virgin)

*M.189, before the text edition
Maria Antoinette Evans Fund (M32073)

M.189, 1511 edition with Latin text
Katherine Eliot Bullard Fund (68.214)

M.189, after 1511, without text, f
Harvey D. Parker Collection (P110)

B.78   Joachim and the Angel (Life of the Virgin)

*M.190, before the text edition
Maria Antoinette Evans Fund (M32074)

M.190, 1511 edition with Latin text
Katherine Eliot Bullard Fund (68.215)

M.190, after 1511, without text, h
Harvey D. Parker Collection (P111)

**B.79   Joachim and Anna Meeting at the Golden Gate
        (Life of the Virgin)**

M.191, before the text edition, a
Katherine Eliot Bullard Fund (68.211)

*M.191, before the text edition, b
Maria Antoinette Evans Fund (M32075)

M.191, 1511 edition with Latin text
Katherine Eliot Bullard Fund (68.216)

M.191, after 1511, without text, g(?)
Harvey D. Parker Collection (P112)

B.80   Birth of the Virgin (Life of the Virgin)

*M.192, before the text edition, a
Centennial Gift of Landon T. Clay (68.194)

*M.192, before the text edition, b
Maria Antoinette Evans Fund (M32076)

M.192, 1511 edition with Latin text
Katherine Eliot Bullard Fund (68.217)

M.192, after 1511, without text, h
Harvey D. Parker Collection (P113)

B.81   Presentation of the Virgin in the Temple (Life of the Virgin)

*M.193, before the text edition, a
Maria Antoinette Evans Fund (M32077)

*M.193, 1511 edition with Latin text
Katherine Eliot Bullard Fund (68.218)

M.193, after 1511, without text, e–g
Harvey D. Parker Collection (P114)

M.193, after 1511, without text, h
Gift of Mrs. T. Jefferson Coolidge, by sale of duplicates
(68.277)

B.82   Betrothal of the Virgin (Life of the Virgin)

*M.194, before the text edition
Maria Antoinette Evans Fund (M32078)

M.194, before the text edition
Bequest of Mrs. Horatio G. Curtis (M35521)

M.194, 1511 edition with Latin text
Katherine Eliot Bullard Fund (68.219)

M.194, after 1511, without text, e
Harvey D. Parker Collection (P115)

B.83   Annunciation (Life of the Virgin)

*M.195, before the text edition, b
Maria Antoinette Evans Fund (M32079)

M.195, 1511 edition with Latin text
Katherine Eliot Bullard Fund (68.220)

M.195, after 1511, without text, f
Harvey D. Parker Collection (P116)

B.84   Visitation (Life of the Virgin)

*M.196, before the text edition
Maria Antoinette Evans Fund (M32080)

M.196, before the text edition
Centennial Gift of Landon T. Clay (68.195)

M.196, 1511 edition with Latin text
Katherine Eliot Bullard Fund (68.221)

M.196, after 1511, without text, b
Harvey D. Parker Collection (P117)

B.85   Nativity (Life of the Virgin)

*M.197, before the text edition, b
Maria Antoinette Evans Fund (M32081)

M.197, 1511 edition with Latin text
Katherine Eliot Bullard Fund (68.222)

M.197, after 1511, without text, c
Harvey D. Parker Collection (P118)

B.86   Circumcision (Life of the Virgin)

*M.198, before the text edition, a–b
Maria Antoinette Evans Fund (M32082)

M.198, before the text edition, b
Katherine Eliot Bullard Fund (68.212)

M.198, 1511 edition with Latin text
Katherine Eliot Bullard Fund (68.223)

M.198, after 1511, without text, b
Harvey D. Parker Collection (P119)

B.87   Adoration of the Magi (Life of the Virgin)

*M.199, before the text edition, b
Maria Antoinette Evans Fund (M32083)

M.199, 1511 edition with Latin text
Katherine Eliot Bullard Fund (68.224)

M.199, after 1511, without text, c
Harvey D. Parker Collection (P121)

B.88   Presentation of Christ (Life of the Virgin)

*M.200, before the text edition
Maria Antoinette Evans Fund (M32084)

M.200, before the text edition
Harvey D. Parker Collection (P122)

M.200, 1511 edition with Latin text
Katherine Eliot Bullard Fund (68.225)

M.200, after 1511, without text, e(?)
Harvey D. Parker Fund, by sale of duplicates (68.262)

B.89   Flight into Egypt (Life of the Virgin)

*M.201, before the text edition, b–c
Maria Antoinette Evans Fund (M32085)

M.201, 1511 edition with Latin text
Katherine Eliot Bullard Fund (68.226)

M.201, after 1511, without text, d
Bequest of Francis Bullard (M24891)

M.201, after 1511, without text, f
Harvey D. Parker Collection (P123)

B.90 **Sojourn of the Holy Family in Egypt (Life of the Virgin)**
M.202, before the text edition, a
Centennial Gift of Landon T. Clay (68.196)

*M.202, before the text edition, b
Maria Antoinette Evans Fund (M32086)

M.202, 1511 edition with Latin text
Katherine Eliot Bullard Fund (68.227)

M.202, after 1511, without text, i
Harvey D. Parker Collection (P124)

B.91 **Christ among the Doctors (Life of the Virgin)**
*M.203, before the text edition
Maria Antoinette Evans Fund (M32087)

M.203, before the text edition
Bequest of Francis Bullard (M24892)

M.203, 1511 edition with Latin text
Katherine Eliot Bullard Fund (68.228)

M.203, after 1511, without text, g
Harvey D. Parker Collection (P125)

B.92 **Christ Taking Leave from his Mother (Life of the Virgin)**
*M.204, before the text edition, a
Maria Antoinette Evans Fund (M32083)

M.204, 1511 edition with Latin text
Gift of the Estate of G. R. Nutter (38.91)

M.204, 1511 edition with Latin text
Katherine Eliot Bullard Fund (68.229)

B.93 **Death of the Virgin (Life of the Virgin)**
*M.205, before the text edition, a
Maria Antoinette Evans Fund (M32090)

M.205, before the text edition, b
Harvey D. Parker Collection (P127)

M.205, 1511 edition with Latin text
Katherine Eliot Bullard Fund (68.230)

B.94 **Assumption and Coronation of the Virgin (Life of the Virgin)**
*M.206, before the text edition
Maria Antoinette Evans Fund (M32091)

M.206, before the text edition
Harvey D. Parker Collection (P128)

M.206, 1511 edition with Latin text
Katherine Eliot Bullard Fund (68.231)

*M.206, after 1511, without text, c
Harvey D. Parker Fund, by sale of duplicates (68.263)

B.95 **Glorification of the Virgin (Life of the Virgin)**
*M.207, before the text edition, a
Maria Antoinette Evans Fund (M32089)

M.207, before the text edition, a
Harvey D. Parker Collection (P129)

M.207, 1511 edition with Latin text
Katherine Eliot Bullard Fund (68.232)

B.96 **Holy Family with Joachim and Saint Ann**
M.215a
Harvey D. Parker Collection (P131)

B.97 **Holy Kinship with Two Musical Angels**
M.216a
Bequest of Francis Bullard (M24893)

B.98 **Madonna with Saint Joseph, Saint Ann and Three Small Children**
M.217a(?)
Helen and Alice Colburn Fund (M33023)

B.99 **Holy Family with Five Angels**
M.214a
Maria Antoinette Evans Fund (M32603)

M.214d(?)
Harvey D. Parker Collection (P134)

B.100 **Holy Family with Two Angels in a Vaulted Hall**
M.213b(?)
Harvey D. Parker Collection (P135)

B.101 **The Virgin as Queen of the Angels**
*M.211a
Stephen Bullard Memorial Fund (40.13)

M.211e(?)
Harvey D. Parker Collection (P186)

B.102 **Holy Family with Three Hares**
*M.212a
Maria Antoinette Evans Fund (M32604)

*M.212c
Harvey D. Parker Collection (P3355)

*M.212i
Bequest of William P. Babcock (B116)

B.103 **Saint Christopher**
M.223a
Harvey D. Parker Collection (P139)

B.104 **Saint Christopher with the Flight of Birds**
M.222e
Harvey D. Parker Collection (P141)

B.107 **Saints Anthony and Paul in the Desert**
M.221a
Harvey D. Parker Collection (P142)

B.108 **Saints Stephen, Sixtus, and Lawrence**
M.235c(?)
Harvey D. Parker Collection (P143)

B.110 **Saint Francis Receiving the Stigmata**
M.224b(?)
Harvey D. Parker Collection (P145)

B.111 **Saint George on Horseback**
*M.225b
Stephen Bullard Memorial Fund (68.245)

M.225d(?)
Harvey D. Parker Collection (P146)

B.112 **Saint John the Baptist and Saint Onuphrius**
M.230a
Bequest of Mrs. Henry Lee Higginson, Sr., by sale of duplicates (68.274)

M.230e
Harvey D. Parker Collection (P147)

B.113 Saint Jerome in a Cave

*M.229, I, a
Samuel Putnam Avery Fund (M28550)

M.229, I, b
Harvey D. Parker Collection (P149)

*M.229, I, C, c
Harvey D. Parker Collection (P150)

*M.229, II, b
Harvey D. Parker Collection (P151)

B.114 Saint Jerome in His Cell

*M.228a
Bequest of Francis Bullard (M24894)

B.116 The Patron Saints of Austria

M.219, II, b
Harvey D. Parker Collection (P153)

B.117 Martyrdom of the Ten Thousand

*M.218a
Stephen Bullard Memorial Fund (65.1024)

M.218c–e
Harvey D. Parker Collection (P3357)

B.118 Saints Nicholas, Ulrich, and Erasmus

M.233c
Bequest of Francis Bullard (M24895)

B.119 David in Penitence

M.108c–d
Harvey D. Parker Collection (P156)

B.120 Martyrdom of Saint Catherine

M.236g
Harvey D. Parker Collection (P3358)

Electrotype impression
Gift of the Trustees of the Metropolitan Museum of Art
(M28469)

B.121 Elevation of Saint Magdalen

M.237b–e(?)
Maria Antoinette Evans Fund (M32605)

M.237c–f(?)
Harvey D. Parker Collection (P158)

B.122 The Trinity

*M.187b–c
Bequest of Francis Bullard (M24896)

M.187e(?)
Special Purchase Fund, 1905 (M20354)

B.123 The Mass of Saint Gregory

*M.226a
Stephen Bullard Memorial Fund (M28699)

*M.226e–f
Harvey D. Parker Collection (P160)

B.125 Martyrdom of Saint John the Baptist

M.231c(?)
Harvey D. Parker Collection (P162)

**B.126 Salome Bringing the Head of Saint John the Baptist
to Her Mother Herodias**

M.232a(?)
Gift of Mrs. C. Tunnard in Memory of W. G. Russell Allen
(61.1356)

M.232g(?)
Harvey D. Parker Collection (P163)

B.127 Hercules

*M.238, I, a
Maria Antoinette Evans Fund (M32606)

M.238, I, d
Katherine Eliot Bullard Fund (68.276)

M.238, II, a
Harvey D. Parker Collection (P164)

B.128 The Bath House

*M.266b
Bequest of Francis Bullard (M24897)

M.266d
Harvey D. Parker Collection (P166)

B.131 Knight on Horseback and Lansquenet

*M.265, I
Stephen Bullard Memorial Fund (68.246)

*M.265, II, c(?)
Bequest of Francis Bullard (M24898)

M.265, II, d
Harvey D. Parker Collection (P167)

B.132 Lansquenet and Death

M.239, I, c(?)
Maria Antoinette Evans Fund (M32607)

M.239, II, b(?)
Harvey D. Parker Collection (P168)

B.133 The School Teacher

*M.267, I, b
William A. Sargent Fund (46.4)

B.136 Rhinoceros

*M.273, I
Stephen Bullard Memorial Fund (68.247)

M.273, VI
Harvey D. Parker Collection (P170)

*M.273, VII
Bequest of W. G. Russell Allen (1971.235)

B.137 Siege of a Fortress

M.272d
Gift of Mrs. C. Tunnard in Memory of W. G. Russell Allen
(61.1357)

B.138 Triumphal Arch of Maximilian

*M.251, first edition, 36 sheets
Otis Norcross Fund (51.415)

M.251, fourth edition
Frederick Keppel Memorial Bequest (M23584, 1–46)

"The Meeting of Maximilian I and Henry VIII"
M.251, separate printing, A
Stephen Bullard Memorial Fund (M28700)

Books

*1527, October, Nuremberg, **Etliche underricht, zu befestigung der Stett, Schloss und flecken (Treatise on the Fortification of Towns, Castles, and Places)**
[Hieronymus Andreä]
Meder XXVIII, 1527, first German edition, A
Bound with Dürer's *Underweysung der messung . . .,* 1525
Samuel Putnam Avery Fund (Book Register 2973, 38.1618)

*1538, Nuremberg, Albrecht Dürer, **Underweysung der Messung, mit dem Zirckel und richtscheyt . . . (Teaching of Measurement with Compass and Ruler . . .)**
Hieronymus Formschneyder [Andreä]
Meder XXVI, 1538, third German edition
Horatio Greenough Curtis Fund (Book Register 1650)

*1538, Nuremberg, Albrecht Dürer, **Underweysung der Messung, mit dem Zirckel und richtscheyt . . . (Teaching of Measurement with Compass and Ruler . . .)**
Hieronymus Formschneyder [Andreä]
Meder XXVI, 1538, third German edition (incomplete copy)
Bound with Sebastien Münster's *Fürmalung und künstlich Beschreibung der Horologien,* Basel, Heinrich Peter, 1544
Gift of Sylvester R. Koehler (K216)

*1604 (sic), Arnheim, Albrecht Dürer, **Opera Alberti Düreri (Works of Albrecht Dürer)**
Johann Janssen
Meder XXVI, 1603, fourth German edition
Gift of Thomas Gaffield (Book Register 480, M2852)

COUNTY COLLEGE OF MORRIS
LEARNING RESOURCES CENTER

R00027 76453